*The American
Immigration Collection*

The School
and
the Immigrant

HERBERT ADOLPHUS MILLER

Arno Press and *The New York Times*

NEW YORK 1970

Reprint Edition 1970 by Arno Press Inc.

Reprinted from a copy in
The Kansas State University Library

LC# 71-129507

ISBN 0-405-00561-X

The American Immigration Collection—Series II
ISBN for complete set 0-405-00543-1

Manufactured in the United States of America

THE SCHOOL AND THE IMMIGRANT

CLEVELAND EDUCATION SURVEY

THE SCHOOL AND THE IMMIGRANT

BY

HERBERT ADOLPHUS MILLER

PROFESSOR OF SOCIOLOGY
OBERLIN COLLEGE

THE SURVEY COMMITTEE OF THE
CLEVELAND FOUNDATION
CLEVELAND · OHIO

20   1916

WM· F· FELL CO· PRINTERS
PHILADELPHIA

FOREWORD

This report on "The School and the Immigrant" is one of the 25 sections of the report of the Education Survey of Cleveland conducted by the Survey Committee of the Cleveland Foundation in 1915. Twenty-three of these sections will be published as separate monographs. In addition there will be a larger volume giving a summary of the findings and recommendations relating to the regular work of the public schools, and a second similar volume giving the summary of those sections relating to industrial education. Copies of all these publications may be obtained from the Cleveland Foundation. They may also be obtained from the Division of Education of the Russell Sage Foundation, New York City. A complete list will be found in the back of this volume, together with prices.

TABLE OF CONTENTS

LIST OF TABLES

LIST OF DIAGRAMS

THE SCHOOL AND THE IMMIGRANT

CHAPTER I

CLEVELAND AS A FOREIGN CITY

Cleveland is one of the most foreign cities in the United States. Of the 50 cities having a population of over 100,000 inhabitants at the time of the last census, only seven—New York, Chicago, Boston, Paterson, Fall River, Lowell, and Bridgeport—contained a larger proportion of foreign inhabitants. Cleveland's foreign population would constitute by itself a city larger than any other in the state of Ohio except Cincinnati, and equalled or surpassed in size by only 28 other cities in the entire country.

The rate of increase in the foreign population has closely followed the general growth of the city. The proportion of foreign born inhabitants to the total population has varied but slightly during the past quarter of a century. When the census of 1890 was taken, 37.5 per cent of the total white population was foreign. In 1910 the proportion had decreased to 35.5 per cent, a shift of only two per cent in 20 years.

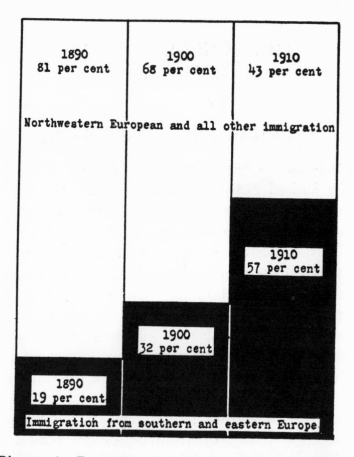

Diagram 1.—Proportion of the foreign born population in Cleveland from the countries of southern and eastern Europe and from all other countries in 1890, 1900, and 1910

Although the ratio of foreign to native born has been fairly constant, quite the contrary is true with respect to the sources from which the foreign element is drawn. In 1890 nearly three-quarters of all the foreign born population of the city were from northern and western Europe, and over one-third were from countries in which the national language is English. During the last two decades of the past century the tide of immigration shifted and there has been an ever-increasing number of immigrants from southern and eastern Europe, while the proportion from English-speaking countries steadily decreased. This change in the composition of the foreign population is shown graphically in Diagram 1.

In 1890 there were about 71,000 foreigners in Cleveland from the northern and western European countries. The number increased to approximately 76,000 in the following decade, but from 1900 to 1910 not only was there no increase, but the census shows an actual loss of nearly 2,000, although the whole population of the city nearly doubled during the same period. On the other hand, the number drawn from southern and eastern Europe, which was about 18,000 in 1890, increased during the following two decades over 600 per cent, or more than 13 times as rapidly as the general increase in population, reaching a total in 1910 of nearly 112,000. In 1890 natives of southern and eastern European countries constituted less than one-fifth of the total foreign population of the city; in 1910 they constituted nearly three-fifths of the total.

The number from each of the principal countries at the end of the three last census periods —1890, 1900, and 1910—is shown in Diagram 2. In 1890 and 1900, Germany led, with the English-speaking countries—the British Isles and Canada—a close second. During the decade 1900–10, the immigration from Austria, Hungary, Russia, and Italy increased at a tremendous rate, so that in 1910 the Austrians led in point of numbers, with a total of 42,059, an increase of 23,078 over 1900. During the same period the number of Hungarians increased from 9,558 to 31,503, the Russians from 7,726 to 25,477, and the Italians from 3,065 to 10,836. Of the 97,000 foreigners in Cleveland in 1890, less than two-thirds came from non-English-speaking countries; in 1910 the proportion had risen to considerably more than four-fifths.

A LARGE PROPORTION CANNOT SPEAK ENGLISH

Without going into a detailed study of the social and educational characteristics of the old and the new immigration, we may take up briefly two points of peculiar significance from the

14

standpoint of public education. The first relates
to the ability to speak English. The successful

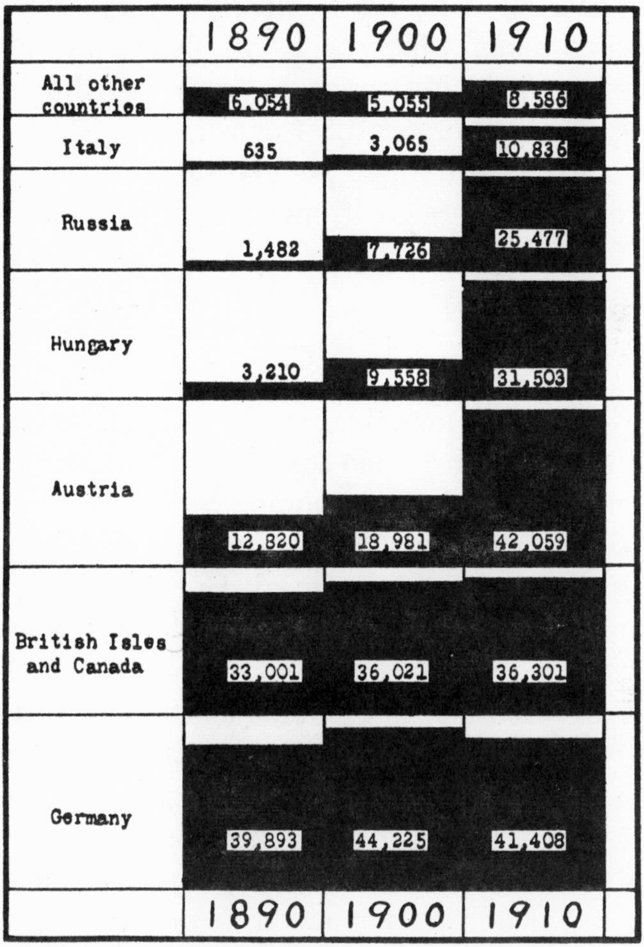

	1890	1900	1910	
All other countries	6,054	5,055	8,586	
Italy	635	3,065	10,836	
Russia	1,482	7,726	25,477	
Hungary	3,210	9,558	31,503	
Austria	12,820	18,981	42,059	
British Isles and Canada	33,001	36,021	36,301	
Germany	39,893	44,225	41,408	
	1890	1900	1910	

Diagram 2.—Number of people of foreign birth from various
countries in 1890, 1900, and 1910

assimilation of the immigrant, his adaptation to
American customs and ways of thought, and

15

to a marked degree his economic and social status, depend on his ability to read and speak the English language. Nearly every disadvantage under which he labors during his first years in this country can be traced in the last analysis to ignorance of English.

Cleveland's foreign population is becoming increasingly foreign from the standpoint of ability to read, write, speak, and understand the English language. In 1900 less than one-fifth of the foreigners in the city 10 years old and over were unable to speak English; in 1910 the proportion of non-English-speaking foreigners had risen to nearly one-third of the total.

Diagram 3 shows a comparison of the proportion of the white foreign population 10 years old and over unable to speak English in the 10 cities of the United States having the largest number of foreign inhabitants in 1910. In this comparison Cleveland stands at the foot of the list, with a per cent of 31.3, or nearly one-third. In proportion to its total foreign population there are over one and one-fourth as many unable to speak English as in Chicago, nearly one and two-fifths as many as in New York, and approximately three times as many as in Boston.

There is no obvious explanation of this abnormal situation. It is true that the greater proportion of English and Irish immigrants in

Boston and the heavy immigration from Canada in border cities like Detroit and Buffalo are factors which make for a low proportion of

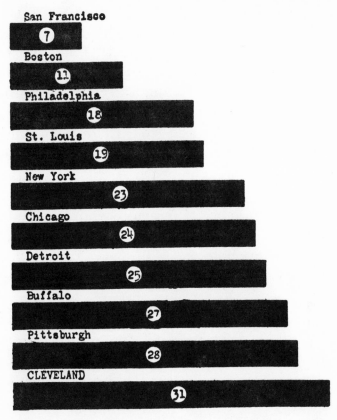

Diagram 3.—Per cent of the foreign population unable to speak English in the 10 American cities having the largest foreign population in 1910

non-English-speaking inhabitants in those cities. But this explanation does not apply to such cities as New York, Chicago, and St. Louis, where the proportion of immigrants from English-speaking countries is practically the same as in Cleveland.

New York more closely resembles Cleveland in the distribution of its foreign population with respect to country of birth than any of the other cities compared. The proportion from northwestern Europe is almost exactly the same in both cities; in the proportions from southern and eastern Europe and from English-speaking countries the differences are negligible. It is almost inexplicable in view of the close similarity as to country of birth and language that the relative number of foreign born inhabitants unable to speak English in Cleveland should so greatly outnumber those in New York. The conclusion seems inevitable that the city's low standing as to the number of its foreign inhabitants who were unable to speak English at the time of the last census is not due to such factors as the nationality or mother tongue of the various groups that make up the foreign population.

FEWER BECOME AMERICAN CITIZENS

There are at the present time between 60,000 and 65,000 men in Cleveland who are not citizens of the United States. Of every 100 men of voting age in 1910, approximately 30 possessed no political rights or interests in this country and owed no allegiance to the government of the United States. In no more important respect does the new immigration from southern and eastern Europe differ from the old immigration from northern and western Europe than in its tendency to cling to an alien political status and indifference to the privileges and duties of American citizenship.

In recent years there has been a marked change for the worse in this respect throughout the entire country, but in few of the larger cities has the downward trend been more pronounced than in Cleveland. Of the 10 American cities having the largest foreign population in 1910, only two — Philadelphia and Pittsburgh — showed a higher proportion of foreign men who had taken no steps to obtain American citizenship. In 1900 the proportion of foreign born males 21 years old or over who were naturalized or had taken out their first naturalization papers in Cleveland was 69 per cent; in 1910 it had dropped to a little over 51 per cent. This falling off in the percentage of naturalization was exceeded only in Detroit among the 10 cities. The per cent in each city who in 1910 had taken no steps toward securing American citizenship is shown graphically in Diagram 4, with a corresponding comparison for 1900. In every case

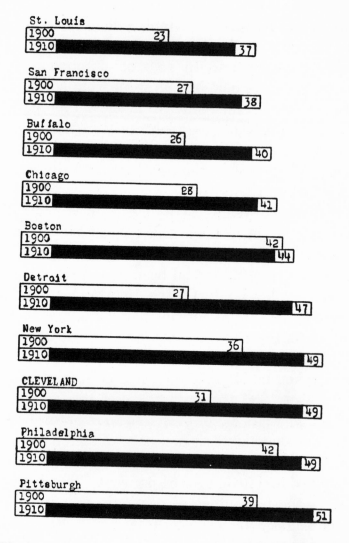

Diagram 4.—Per cent of the foreign male population 21 years old and over who had not taken out naturalization papers in the 10 American cities having the largest foreign populations. Bars in outline show the per cent in 1900; bars in black the per cent in 1910

20

the figures show a decrease in the proportion of naturalization although the amount of variation between the two census periods differs widely. St. Louis leads with 37 per cent, Pittsburgh ranking lowest with 51. Cleveland, which ranks eighth among the 10 cities, shows only a slightly smaller percentage of naturalization than New York, but a much greater loss for the decade.

The present standing of the city in this particular is less disquieting than the marked retrogressive trend the data reveal. The fact that the social and political assimilation of the great mass of aliens in the city is proceeding at a steadily decreasing pace is of the gravest import in its relation to the future welfare of the city.

SUMMARY

Cleveland is one of the most foreign cities in the United States. The proportion of foreign-born has varied but slightly during the past 25 years, but the proportion of foreign inhabitants from the countries of southern and eastern Europe has increased very rapidly, while that from northern and western Europe shows a marked decrease.

The foreign population has become increasingly foreign from the standpoint of ability to speak and read the English language. In none of the 10 cities having the largest number of foreign inhabitants at the time of the last census was the proportion unable to speak English so large as in Cleveland.

In 1910 nearly one-third of all the men of voting age in Cleveland were aliens, possessing no political rights in this country and owing no allegiance to the government of the United States. Conditions in this respect are worse in Cleveland than in most of the larger cities of the country.

CHAPTER II

SCHOOL CHILDREN FROM NON-ENGLISH-SPEAKING HOMES

In the course of the Survey an investigation was made to determine the number of children enrolled in the public schools who were from homes in which English is not regularly spoken. Each child in the schools above the kindergarten age was asked to fill out a blank containing two questions: first, "What is the language of your home?" and second, "What language besides English can you read?" It was assumed that "the language of the home" is the one regularly spoken by the child before he goes to school and to a large extent throughout the years he is in school. The results of studies in other cities have shown that "language of the home" is a better index of "foreignness" among school children than is furnished by the data giving the countries of birth of the parents.

The data were collected from all schools on a single day, and the totals represent the attendance for that day, not the entire number enrolled in the schools. In all, replies were obtained from 75,046 children in the elementary

23

schools, and from 9,088 attending the high schools. Almost exactly one-half of the children in the elementary schools came from homes in which English is not regularly spoken. The most important of the foreign languages on the basis of number of children reporting it as their home language was German. Yiddish comes next, with Bohemian third. More than four-fifths of the foreign children were from homes in which either German, Yiddish, Bohemian, Italian, Hungarian, or Polish was spoken. Only four other languages—Slovak, Slovenian, Russian, and Hebrew—were reported by more than one per cent of the foreign pupils. The distribution is shown in detail in Table 1.

It is probable that in many cases the figures are too low. Frequently it was discovered that the children replied "English" when the parents only understood English, but did not speak it. Many foreign children wish to appear "American," even if exact truthfulness suffers in the process. Some were especially reluctant to acknowledge their native language at the present time on account of the European war. In addition there are many who have a speaking knowledge of some foreign language, even when English is commonly used in the home. It is probable that the total number who can speak a language other than English is from five to

TABLE 1.—LANGUAGES SPOKEN IN HOMES OF PUPILS IN THE
PUBLIC SCHOOLS, CLEVELAND, 1915

Language	Elementary	High	Total
English	37,454	6,325	43,779
German	8,118	1,093	9,211
Yiddish	6,219	576	6,795
Bohemian	5,325	374	5,699
Italian	4,493	108	4,601
Hungarian	3,686	102	3,788
Polish	3,523	113	3,636
Slovak	1,558	40	1,598
Slovenian	1,217	22	1,239
Russian	913	44	957
Hebrew	656	120	776
Swedish	328	40	368
Croatian	218	..	218
Dutch	173	9	182
Roumanian	151	8	159
Lithuanian	147	1	148
Syrian	140	2	142
Finnish	103	6	109
Welsh	80	26	106
French	79	12	91
Norse	59	8	67
Greek	56	1	57
Danish	55	9	64
Ruthenian	43	..	43
Albanian	40	2	42
Serbian	30	1	31
Armenian	27	..	27
Bulgarian	17	..	17
Chinese	15	2	17
Spanish	12	5	17
Other foreign languages	111	23	134
Total	75,046	9,088	84,134

10 per cent greater than the returns obtained
show.

The reluctance of the child to confess his
foreign origin as he becomes older and more
self-conscious is no doubt responsible to some
extent for the marked falling off in the upper

grades. This tendency is illustrated in Diagram 5 which shows the number in each grade from English- and from non-English-speaking homes. In the first grade the number of children from homes in which a foreign language is spoken exceeds those from English-speaking homes by nearly 28 per cent. The numerical superiority of the foreign group continues up to the fifth grade, where it drops considerably below the English-speaking group, with a constantly decreasing ratio up to the eighth grade, in which the children from foreign language homes falls to less than 63 per cent of the number from English-speaking homes.

Although this unfavorable showing is due in some slight degree to inaccuracies in the replies obtained from the children and to the fact that the parents of the older pupils usually have been in this country a considerable time, and therefore are more likely to have learned English, the comparison undoubtedly emphasizes a condition that must be constantly borne in mind in connection with teaching children of foreign parentage. The average child of foreign parentage is not likely to remain in school as long as the average child of native parents, and many of them reach the end of the compulsory attendance period before they have completed the elementary course. During the high school

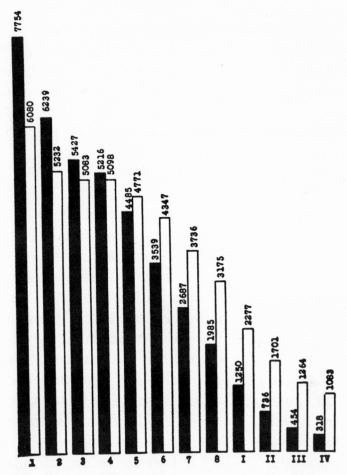

Diagram 5.—Number of children in each grade from homes in which a foreign language is spoken, and number from English-speaking homes. Bars in black represent children from foreign homes; bars in outline children from English-speaking homes

27

period the tendency of the child of foreign parents to leave school is still more in evidence. By the fourth high school year the number of pupils from homes where a foreign language is spoken is reduced to less than one-third the number from English-speaking families. Not only do fewer pupils from foreign homes enter high school, but a very much smaller proportion complete the four-year course.

NUMBER OF ELEMENTARY PUPILS WHO CAN READ SOME FOREIGN LANGUAGE

It was found that approximately one-third of the children from foreign-language-speaking homes were able to read another language besides English. With the exception of German, which is taught in the upper elementary grades and in the high school, this reading knowledge is obtained entirely outside of the public school. The figures of Table 2 present the facts but do not include the pupils of the first and second grades, as it is obvious that there can be no appreciable reading knowledge below the third grade.

German leads in point of numbers and shows a higher ratio to the number of children from homes in which it is spoken than any other language except Hebrew. The ratio of those

28

TABLE 2.—NUMBER OF CHILDREN IN THE ELEMENTARY SCHOOLS FROM THE THIRD TO THE EIGHTH INCLUSIVE WHO CAN READ A FOREIGN LANGUAGE, AND PER CENT THEY ARE OF THE NUMBER IN THESE GRADES FROM HOMES IN WHICH EACH SPECIFIED LANGUAGE IS SPOKEN

Language	Number	Per cent
German	4,901	90
Yiddish	1,479	36
Bohemian	1,278	36
Polish	1,078	57
Hungarian	956	45
Hebrew	925	222
Italian	536	21
Slovak	449	47
Russian	248	43
Slovenian	162	29
Swedish	96	44
Croatian	49	49
Dutch	40	36
Roumanian	26	32
Greek	24	60
French	17	34
Syrian	15	22
Finnish	13	25
Norse	13	37
Ruthenian	12	55
Danish	11	27
Lithuanian	11	17
Welsh	8	17
Serbian	7	54
Spanish	5	63
Chinese	4	67
Armenian	4	29
Bulgarian	3	38
Other foreign languages	62	97

who can read Hebrew to those who come from Hebrew-speaking families is more than two to one. Only a little over one-third of the Yiddish and Bohemian children can read Yiddish or Bohemian, while over one-half of the Poles and nearly one-half of the Hungarians can read their respective languages. Among the more important foreign groups the Italians show the smallest proportion who can read as well as speak their language.

TABLE 3.—NUMBER OF CHILDREN IN THE HIGH SCHOOLS WHO CAN READ A FOREIGN LANGUAGE, AND PER CENT THEY ARE OF THE NUMBER IN THESE GRADES FROM HOMES IN WHICH EACH SPECIFIED LANGUAGE IS SPOKEN

Language	Number	Per cent
German	1,790	164
Yiddish	323	56
Bohemian	205	55
Hebrew	112	90
Polish	80	71
Hungarian	78	70
Italian	54	50
Slovak	44	110
Swedish	34	85
Russian	26	57
French	17	142
Slovenian	13	59
Dutch	5	56
Greek	5	500
Welsh	4	15
Norse	4	50
Finnish	3	50
Chinese	2	100
Spanish	2	40
Roumanian	2	25
Serbian	2	200
Lithuanian	1	100
Danish	1	11
Syrian	1	50
Other foreign languages	4	16

In the high schools one and two-fifths times as many students read German as there are pupils from German-speaking homes. This is due to the fact that German is offered as an elective in the high schools. Over half of the enrollment from Yiddish and Bohemian families and seven-tenths from Polish and Hungarian families read the language of their parents. The distribution is shown in detail in Table 3. It is to be noted that the percentage figures of the lower part of this table are of little significance on account of the small numbers involved.

Foreign Language Teaching in Parochial Schools

Data relating to private schools were secured only from those supported by the Lutherans and the Roman Catholics. The Lutherans have 15 schools, of which one is Slovak and the rest German. The Slovak school, enrolling 359 pupils, comprises but three grades, although it is proposed to open additional grades as soon as capable teachers for them can be secured. Eleven of the 14 German schools reported an attendance of 2,074 in all. The three from which data were not secured are small schools, but it is doubtless well within the actual figures to put the total, in round numbers, at 2,500. Nearly all of these schools have eight grades, and according to the reports of high school principals, they prepare their children well. The universal practice is to teach German one and a quarter hours a day throughout the eight grades. Part of this time is devoted to instruc-

31

tion in religion. All the pupils are able to read, write, and speak German easily when they graduate.

It was somewhat more difficult to secure information from the Catholic schools, but the figures here presented are approximately correct, although in many cases they are probably too low. Of the 52 parochial schools from which data were obtained, 30 may be classed as foreign language schools. The church itself has no particular enthusiasm for these foreign language schools, enduring rather than fostering them, so that the quality of the work done depends on the interest and capacity of the group which each represents, rather than on any determined and standardized educational policy of the church as to foreign language work. This lack of a prevailing purpose and aim in this matter results in considerable disparity in the relative efficiency of the various schools. Table 4 shows the number of children enrolled in the foreign language Catholic schools.

The total enrollment in the Catholic schools is slightly over 28,000, so that the proportion of foreign-language-speaking children is nearly 60 per cent. This, including the 2,859 children in the German and Slovak Lutheran schools, gives a total of at least 20,000 foreign-language-speaking children in the parochial schools.

Adding this number to the enrollment in the public schools gives a grand total of approximately 57,325 children from foreign-language-speaking homes. Those from English-speaking homes enrolled in both public and parochial schools number approximately 50,000.

TABLE 4.—NUMBER OF PUPILS STUDYING THE DIFFERENT FOREIGN LANGUAGES IN THE CATHOLIC SCHOOLS, CLEVELAND, 1915

Language	Number of schools	Pupils enrolled
Polish	6	4,170
German	7	3,977
Bohemian	5	2,850
Slovak	5	2,377
Slovenian	3	1,846
Hungarian	2	1,300
Croatian	1	352
Lithuanian	1	260
Total	30	17,172

The language instruction in the parochial schools is primarily for religious purposes, and is often limited solely to that necessary for learning the catechism. In a few cases the priests are ardent nationalists, and make a real attempt to teach the language.

WIDE VARIATION IN DIFFERENT SCHOOLS

Children from foreign-language-speaking homes are found in every public school in Cleveland.

Doan School, with four German children, three Swedes and one Russian among 795 pupils enrolled, is the least foreign, and Murray Hill, with 1,171 Italians, five Albanians (who also speak Italian), and one German in an enrollment of 1,348, is the most homogeneously foreign of the

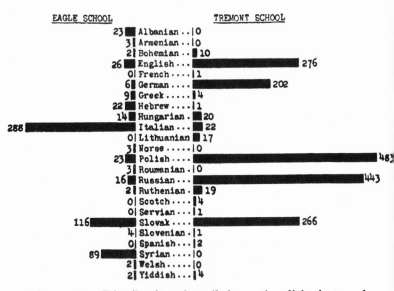

Diagram 6.—Distribution of pupils by nationalities in two elementary schools

elementary schools. Both the percentage of foreign pupils and their distribution by nationality and language vary widely among the different schools, so that the relation of racial and linguistic characteristics to teaching methods and school management becomes a separate problem for each school. The comparison of the

34

foreign distribution in two of the larger elementary schools, Eagle and Tremont, shown in Diagram 6, illustrates this point in a striking way. The Italians are the largest group in the Eagle School, constituting 44 per cent of the total number in the school, while in Tremont only one per cent are Italians. In Tremont the largest group is made up of Polish children, who constitute 27 per cent of the total, as against four per cent in Eagle.

Nor is the problem less complex if only a single school is considered. Such schools as Eagle and Tremont are veritable melting-pots in which the ingredients show no common linguistic or national elements. The proportions given vary also within the schools in the different grades and from year to year.

Summary

Approximately one-half the children in the elementary schools of Cleveland and one-third in the high schools are from homes in which some foreign language is spoken. The children of foreign parentage do not advance so rapidly through the grades as those of native parentage and they drop out much faster in the upper grades. Approximately one-third of the children of foreign parentage can read as well as speak a foreign language. About 20,000 children are receiving instruction in some foreign language in the parochial schools of the city. The distribution of pupils of foreign parentage varies widely in the different public schools and among the different grades in single schools.

CHAPTER III

EFFORTS OF NATIONAL GROUPS TO PRESERVE THEIR LANGUAGES

Each national group expresses its group consciousness in varying degrees of effort to preserve its language by providing more or less adequate instruction for the children in the mother tongue. Generally there are very strong traditional and historical reasons for devotion to the language. Often the immigrant comes from countries where attempts have been made to substitute the language of foreign rulers for the mother tongue with the result that the preservation of the language has become a matter of patriotism.

A very large proportion of the inhabitants of Cleveland possess a reading and speaking knowledge of some language other than English. More than one-half of the children in the public schools speak, and more than one-third read, some other foreign language. The economic and social value of this knowledge cannot be denied, and in every case, excepting that of German, it has been obtained absolutely without cost to the school system. The possibility of conserving this economic and cultural asset should not be lost to sight, even though we recognize that the main duty of the school is to give the child a thorough English education.

The place of foreign languages in the curriculum of the public schools has been determined in the main by custom and tradition. At one time foreign language instruction was limited almost exclusively to Latin and Greek. Later the study of German and French was introduced, and at present considerable attention is given to Spanish on account of its alleged commercial value. The claims of other languages, several of which are spoken by many thousands of children and adults in Cleveland, are deserving of consideration. In addition to their practical and literary value, they have also a moral value in that their preservation would tend to soften the abrupt transition from foreign to American ideals and ways of thought, and to obviate the breakdown in parental control and discipline often observed in immigrant families. It is probable that before many years the Board of Education will be called upon to decide whether or not instruction in such languages as Bohemian, Italian, Hungarian, and Polish should not be offered in the high schools.

The following pages contain a brief description of the efforts now being made by the various foreign groups in the city to teach their languages to the rising generation, with some mention of the social and educational organizations maintained by each group.

BOHEMIANS

The Bohemians, who constitute one of the largest national groups in Cleveland, are unremitting in their efforts to preserve their language. The work is carried on by two quite distinct groups: the Catholics in the parochial schools, and by national organizations without religious affiliation. The majority of the Bohemians send their children to the public schools, but they also maintain five private schools for instruction in the Bohemian language and history. The children attend these schools for three hours on Saturday or Sunday. Each school has a separate organization but there is a central committee to determine the curriculum and choose the teachers.

On Broadway there is a school of 300 children in four grades; on the west side one having about the same number of pupils in three grades; on Quincy Avenue one with 200 pupils in three grades; on Rice Avenue one with 75 children in five grades; and at Mt. Pleasant one with 60 children in three grades. There is also a Sunday kindergarten on Broadway with 300 children meeting in the afternoon.

For older children there is a young people's club maintaining dramatics, singing, and other cultural activities.

Among 5,325 Bohemian children in the elementary grades, 1,278 say that they can read Bohemian. Above the first three grades almost half of them can read the language and in the high schools the proportion is almost two-thirds. In general this ability to read Bohemian is the result of the organized efforts of the private schools that have been mentioned.

CROATIANS

The Croatians belong to the more recent immigration. While their numbers are small, their community feeling is very strong. There are but 218 children in the public schools. In the parochial schools, which give instruction in the Croatian language, there are 354 children enrolled. A society has recently been formed among the young people of this nationality. Its members range in age from six to 16 years and the object of the organization is to promote the study of the Croatian language.

DANES

There is only a small colony of Danes in Cleveland, and apart from the Sunday schools there are no regular exercises carried on in the Danish tongue. The Danes, like the other Scandinavians, enter easily into the American life and readily adopt our customs and institutions.

GERMANS

The status of the Germans is different from that of any other foreign group. It is the only foreign language in which instruction is given in the public elementary schools. The attitude of the Germans toward their own language has been greatly stimulated by the interest taken in it by non-German-speaking people. Altogether there are in the public schools some 9,211 children from German-speaking families and more than half of these young people can read the language as well as speak it. In addition there are about 6,500 more such children in the Catholic and Lutheran schools.

GREEKS

There are only 57 children in the public schools in whose families Greek is regularly spoken, and of these only 24 can read the language. Within

41

the past few years a considerable number of Greek women have come to Cleveland and in the near future the number of Greek children in the schools will rapidly increase. The Greeks are the only foreign group in Cleveland which has not formed any organization centering around national consciousness and aspirations.

Hebrew and Yiddish

The Hebrew- and Yiddish-speaking children should be classed together. All who speak Hebrew also know Yiddish. The number from Hebrew-speaking families is 776 and those from Yiddish-speaking ones is 6,795, making a total of 7,571. There are a great many more who know how to speak Yiddish, yet do not regularly use it, and still others who belong to the same general group but do not speak either language. The effort to maintain Hebrew is so closely related to the religion of the Orthodox Jews that it can hardly be separated from their social and religious lives. The orthodox service is conducted entirely in Hebrew and from time immemorial it has been the custom of the Jews to employ private teachers to instruct their children in Hebrew.

In one public school in the Woodland Avenue district where more than nine-tenths of the children are Jewish, from one-half to two-thirds of the pupils have had this sort of private instruction in both Hebrew and Yiddish. The instruction in the former language is frequently most inadequate, often consisting of simply learning to read without understanding. When one knows the Hebrew letters, Yiddish seems to be acquired very easily. It is a language composed of elements of the various languages of the countries in which the Jews have lived and it is now appropriating many English words.

Yiddish literature, which is not over 50 years old, is growing very rapidly. There are many newspapers in the language and one daily— "The Jewish World"—is published in Cleveland. Interest in Hebrew is also reviving and it is rapidly becoming a modern living language instead of an exclusively classical and religious one. There are several newspapers published in Hebrew and a modern literature is developing.

There are now in the city three schools in which Hebrew is taught by modern methods. The oldest and largest one has eight grades and is located on 35th Street, between Woodland and Scovill Avenues. There is another school on 55th Street and one on 105th Street. The children attend every afternoon after regular school hours, on Sundays, and all day during the summer. While the attendance is not abso-

43

lutely regular, the rooms are crowded to capacity. The instructors are mostly young men who are students in high school or college and have been well instructed in Hebrew before coming to America.

In the first three grades the children attend for one and a half hours a day, while in the upper classes the session lasts for two and a half hours. In the winter months school opens at about half past four and does not close until 8:30 in the evening. In the summer months the session is from nine to one. From 500 to 1,000 pupils are enrolled in the largest school and many more desire to attend than can be accommodated. These schools are secular and while sympathetic with the orthodox religion, they are really nationalistic in purpose.

There are in addition several more or less modern schools connected with synagogues. The Zionist Socialists conduct a school which teaches Yiddish and the orphan asylum on Woodland Avenue has classes in Hebrew.

HUNGARIANS

The Hungarians, with nearly 4,000 children in the public schools, have a historical background for their devotion to their language, but as yet this has not been thoroughly organized. Many

44

of them are Catholic, while the rest belong to several different Protestant denominations. A majority of the children are in the public schools but there are also considerable numbers in the parochial schools.

Three churches maintain classes for instruction in the language, history, and geography of Hungary. During the past summer there were seven classes with 546 children enrolled in the Reformed Church on 79th Street and during the other months of the year a school was maintained on Saturday with more than 150 children in attendance. Not all the pupils are connected with this church. The West Side Reformed Church gives instruction to about 100 children and in the St. John Greek Catholic Church there is a summer school of four grades. Here a few finish the work in four years while the rest continue for five or six years. The children are taught to read and write and to sing their national and religious songs. There is no religious instruction in the summer time, but throughout the rest of the year religious classes are held on Saturday and Sunday in Hungarian.

ITALIANS

There are approximately the same number of Italian children as there are Hungarian children, but since the Italians have no parochial schools their public school enrollment is about 1,000 more than that of the Hungarians. Since there are no opportunities in the city for learning to read Italian, a large part of the children have to get their religious instruction in English although they belong to the Italian Catholic Church. The recent development of national societies of "Sons and Daughters of Italy" is likely to have considerable influence in the preservation of national ideals and traditions. Some of the older Italian children who have attended the public elementary and high schools are now taking up the study of the Italian language.

LITHUANIANS

The Lithuanians have only 148 children in the public schools as compared with 260 in parochial schools. The Lithuanian language belongs in the same class as the Hebrew and Greek. In some respects it more nearly resembles Sanscrit than any other Aryan language although it has appropriated many Slavonic words. It has a literature rich in poetry and folk lore and will probably come into greater importance in the near future.

NORWEGIANS AND SWEDES

The Norwegians, like the Danes, have only a small colony and maintain Norwegian instruction in the Sunday schools. The Swedes are somewhat more numerous, with 328 children in the elementary schools and 40 in the high schools. There are five Protestant churches where the services are conducted in Swedish. There is also a summer school with a six weeks' session three hours a day in which instruction is given in Swedish. On the whole, little effort is made to maintain the language after English is learned.

POLES

There is probably no other people so devoted to maintaining their language as the Poles. In their struggle for independence from Germany and Russia, their language and their religion have become symbols for freedom. It is hard to distinguish between their devotion to their language and to their church. It is estimated that 99 per cent of them are Catholics. More than half of their children are in the parochial schools and almost all of those who attend the public schools also spend some time in the parochial schools. It is reported by the librarians that the Polish children are the only ones who draw juvenile books in their native language for

47

their own reading. It is said that pupils of other nationalities draw foreign books only for their parents.

RUSSIANS AND RUTHENIANS

There are 957 children in the public schools who claim to come from homes where Russian is spoken and 43 from Ruthenian homes. Nevertheless it is probable that there are not more than 100 Russians from Great Russia in the entire city. Almost all of the Russian-speaking families in Cleveland came from Galicia in Austria. Historically this belongs to what is known as "Little Russia." On the Russian side of the border the people are called Ukrainians and on the Galician side Ruthenians. There are some religious divisions that tend to draw the two groups apart. The language uses the same alphabet as the Russians, but differs from official Russian almost as much as Polish and Serbian do. The people belong to the Greek Catholic or Greek Orthodox churches and send their children to the public schools. Both groups maintain schools for teaching their own language. Since the religious services are conducted in old Slavic, instruction in this language is given in the higher grades, while in the lower ones only Russian is taught.

48

ROUMANIANS

Cleveland has been the leading Roumanian city in America although it has now dropped into second place. There are probably some 10,000 of the people in the city. Since most of them are recent arrivals, there are comparatively few of their children in the public schools. The number reported is 159, although this must be an under-statement. Many Roumanians belong to the Greek Orthodox and Greek Catholic churches while others have no religious affiliations. Few of them came from Roumania proper, but instead from Transylvania and Bukowina in Austria-Hungary. Many who learned Hungarian or Magyar in Hungary are now learning Roumanian in America and it is probable that there will be a great increase of interest in the language in the near future.

SERBIANS

The Serbians have only 31 children in the public schools, but nevertheless they are already planning to start a private school in their language. Except for the alphabet, their language is identical with that of the Croatians, but on account of the difference in religion few of the children attend the Croatian parochial school. A library is maintained on St. Clair Avenue by the Serbian Educational Society of New York and there is talk of using the library room for a school with volunteer teachers. Almost none of the Serbians come from Serbia proper but from Austria.

SLOVAKS

There are approximately 1,600 Slovak-speaking children in the public schools and a large number in the parochial schools. The Slovaks coming from Northern Hungary are like the Hungarians in being divided into Catholics and Protestants, but linguistically and nationally they are very closely related to the Bohemians. Approximately half are Roman Catholic. In Hungary they have made a great struggle to maintain their language, and large numbers of them have come to America in the past few years in order to escape oppression at home. There have been some Slovaks in Cleveland for 20 years or more. Like the Roumanians, many of them have learned to read their language since coming to America. Last fall the Slovak paper published in Cleveland was changed from a weekly to a daily. Most Slovak children study Slovak. The Protestant churches maintain afternoon and evening classes throughout the year. The instruction is of a high order and is rapidly improving.

SLOVENIANS

Cleveland has a larger Slovenian population than any other city in America. Practically all of these people have come within the past 20 years and many very recently. There are 1,239 children in the public schools and a somewhat larger number in the parochial schools. So far no classes have been organized for the children to learn the language except in the parochial schools, but the national feeling is being rapidly developed and schools will probably be established in the near future.

SYRIANS

There are only 142 children from Syrian-speaking homes in the public schools, but the Syrians, in spite of their division into four religious groups, have a strong national consciousness. These religious groups are the Catholics, who constitute about one-third; the Maronites, who are a sect of the Catholics; the Greek Orthodox; and a small group of Mohammedans. By mutual agreement many parents who had begun to speak English in the home now speak only Syrian in order that "their children may not get away from them." St. George's Society has bought a house on Cedar Avenue to be used for a school as soon as the money can be raised to

51

maintain it. The majority of the members of this society are Catholics but the activities of the club are not religious and all divisions of the people will use the school.

OTHER GROUPS

There are several other linguistic groups in Cleveland, but they are of less significance than those that have been described. It is interesting to observe in the light of the recent agitation for the introduction of Spanish into the public schools that there are in the city only 17 children from Spanish-speaking families.

USE OF PUBLIC SCHOOL BUILDINGS BY NATIONAL GROUPS

One important problem which should be faced by the Board of Education and the people of Cleveland is the formulation of a policy with respect to offering the use of public school buildings for the nationalistic expressions of the different groups. In the opinion of the writer of the present report, it is important that these buildings should be so used more generally than they are at present. It seems a pity for the Syrians to purchase a house on Cedar Avenue and 22nd Street in order to teach their children the Syrian language when far better quarters are available within two blocks in the Eagle School. Similarly the Hebrew building on 35th Street is used to its utmost capacity for carrying on work that could be done much better in the evening in the Longwood School only three doors away. Among most of the nationalities there are singing and dramatic societies and literary associations which could properly meet in public school buildings and which would in no way interfere with the regular work of the schools.

SUMMARY

The different national groups express their group consciousness through varying degrees of effort to preserve their languages by providing instruction for the children in the mother tongue. More than half of the school children of Cleveland speak some foreign tongue and a large proportion of them read some language other than English.

Most of the important national groups send large numbers of their children to parochial schools conducted in foreign languages. In addition they maintain part-time schools for giving language instruction to those of their children who attend the public schools. These part-time schools hold sessions in the afternoon, in the evening, on Saturdays, on Sundays, and during the summer months.

Many of the national groups are divided into different religious sects and some are split into political divisions having their inception in old-world politics. In order to understand the social and educational problems of the different foreign groups, it is necessary to study their origin and history. The necessity for some special knowledge of this sort is indicated by the fact that many of the immigrants speak the language of one country but come from a different country. Thus the Russian-speaking children in our schools came from Austria; the Roumanians did not come from Roumania but from Austria-Hungary; and almost none of the Serbians came from Serbia.

CHAPTER IV

CHARACTERISTICS OF NATIONAL GROUPS

There is a current belief that the prime qualification of a public school teacher is to know certain school subjects and how to teach them. It must not be forgotten, however, that the human beings she is teaching respond with great readiness to genuine sympathy and understanding and that her real success depends in no small measure on her personal relations with the children in the school. The provincial self-satisfaction which many teachers feel in their Americanism does not help them make good Americans out of their foreign pupils. They seem to fear sometimes that if any affection for foreign traditions and ideals is retained, the child is likely to be less American in his sympathies. Nothing could be farther from the truth. There is the closest relation between the central ideal of Americanism—freedom and liberty—and the principal motive underlying the abandonment of his native land by the immigrant.

With the exception of the Germans and the Italians, many of the immigrants come from subject races and they come here primarily for freedom. It is true that the economic advantage offered by America is the assigned reason for their coming, but the fact that no Roumanians come from Roumania, no Serbians from Serbia, no Russians from Russia, shows that something besides economic influences cause the emigration. Again and again, when the immigrant has been asked for a comparison between this country and his own, the invariable reply has been "America is free."

The immigrant is often criticized for living in segregated groups. No criticism could be more unjust. Is it not perfectly natural everywhere for social groups having something in common to try to live in the same neighborhood? Even should they try to avoid segregation, their American neighbors would not allow it. The result is that every effort is made to keep them from getting into a new section. Nevertheless, as soon as the standard of living is raised, we find all the nationalities breaking away from the original colony.

As a matter of fact, we find within these various colonies a neighborliness and social organization which are sadly lacking in much of our modern society. A teacher should know something of the social life to be found within these various groups, both in order that she may understand her pupils better and that she may be able to use these social forces to the advantage of the school and the community.

In addition she ought to know something of the history of the region from which her pupils or their parents have come. If she knows even a few words of their language, it might prove of inestimable value in establishing a sympathetic relationship between the teachers and the children, but more especially between the parents and the school. A knowledge of the geography of the child's native land would be an asset to teacher and principal. From one school some children were listed as speaking Ukrainian. Now it is true that very few people know the difference between Ruthenian, Russian, and Ukrainian, and in all probability the children themselves did not know. As a matter of fact the Ukrain is a section of the Southwestern part of Russia and the language spoken is a dialect of the Russian and is called not Ukrainian but either Little Russian or Ruthenian. There are at least 35,000,000 who speak this language—certainly enough to justify some knowledge on the part of the teacher as to their existence, particularly since there are over 900 children from this part of Russia in the Cleveland schools.

Again, "Slovenian" figures in the list of

languages used in the investigation conducted by the Survey, and yet some teachers added "Griner." Even granting that the children do not know the difference between Slovenian and Griner, certainly when there are approximately 20,000 Slovenians in Cleveland and over 1,000 in the public schools, principals with a considerable enrollment of Slovenians ought to know that Griner is a name derived from the name of the province of Krain, and that the people themselves generally repudiate its use.

These illustrations show the common indifference of teachers who take it for granted that all they need is a knowledge of the subjects they teach. There are, of course, a considerable number of exceptions. For example, the principal of one school attended by many Italians speaks Italian, and the parents are constantly coming to the school for consultation about their children and for general advice. Certainly this makes possible an Americanizing influence through the school which is far more effective than would be secured by requiring the parents to speak English.

The following pages contain a brief statement as to the national and racial characteristics of the various foreign groups with a few suggestions as to supplementary reading for teachers in charge of classes made up largely of foreign children.

BOHEMIANS

It is impossible to understand the Bohemians in America without some knowledge of Bohemian history. They are one of the national divisions of the Slavs. The Bohemians who dwell in the northwestern part of Austria, directly between Dresden and Vienna, have been the subject of more German influence than any other Slavic people, and in many respects are indistinguishable from the Germans. In 1415 the church and the state burned at the stake John Huss, a Bohemian priest, the first martyr to religious freedom. A revolt took place which made Bohemia Protestant until the Thirty Years War, which began in 1618. After that Catholicism was re-established, and to this day embraces nearly all the inhabitants of Bohemia. In America, beginning more than 50 years ago, a reaction was organized until at the present time approximately two-thirds of an estimated million are aggressive free-thinkers.

In Cleveland about half are Catholics and the rest free-thinkers, with only a few hundred Protestants. Both parties have many organizations and, while the feeling between the two is very strong, the common Slavic feeling manifests itself most strongly in antipathy for the German language. The free-thinkers are the more nationalistic, and fortunately so, for with the loss of the control of the church there is a tendency to materialism which can be counteracted only by devotion to some social cause. There is no group to which the mother tongue and national history can have more moral value. This is in part because their history is peculiarly rich. Commenius, one of the world's greatest educators, was a Bohemian, exiled during the Thirty Years War. The influence of Bohemian history has been such that the people refuse to accept dogma, and even the children argue theology.

The best descriptive book on the Slavs is "Our Slavic Fellow Citizens," by Emily Green Balch, published by the Charities Publication Committee, New York, 1910. This deals with both European and American conditions for Bohemians, Croatians, Russians, Roumanians, Ruthenians, Serbians, Slovaks, and Slovenians.

CROATIANS AND SERBIANS

These two people can be considered together. Their spoken language is the same, but the Croatians are Roman Catholics and use the

Latin alphabet, while the Serbians are Greek Orthodox and use the Cryllic or Greek alphabet. Most of those in America come from exactly the same region in southern Austria-Hungary. In fact the census taker classifies them under one or the other name solely by their religion. They have been dominated by the Hungarians. They, with the Slovenians from the adjoining Austrian provinces, are group-conscious as South Slavs, being entirely separated by Germans and Hungarians from the North Slavs—Bohemians, Slovaks, and Poles. Their deepest purpose is freedom.

FINNS

There happens to be only a small number of Finns in Cleveland, but there are some facts which should be known about them. Finland was for six and a half centuries ruled by Sweden, and since 1809 has belonged to Russia, but the culture has been continuously Swedish until almost the present decade. Now the Finn is claiming his own national individuality and his language is rapidly replacing Swedish. The Finnish language is extremely difficult, and every Finnish child in the schools must learn Russian and many learn Swedish. These languages are all so difficult that they can master

English very quickly. The Finns are almost all Lutheran, and have decidedly socialistic tendencies which are being abated somewhat by the growing nationalism. In cleanliness they are quite the equal of the Dutch. Helsingfors, the capital of Finland, is probably the cleanest city in the world.

GERMANS

A large proportion of the Germans who come from Germany have been in America a long time. A majority of them came for the same purpose of securing freedom that has influenced the other groups. They belong to the earlier immigration and very few have come to this country in recent years. Most people are so familiar with the Germans that it is unnecessary to add anything here except to call attention to the fact that conditions are now tense and the Germans are feeling a self-consciousness which the majority of them did not feel hitherto.

JEWS

The most complex and most variously regarded of all our immigrants are the Jews. The earlier arrivals came from Germany, and many have been here for several generations and occupy a most important place in American life. Later many came from Hungary. With only occasional exceptions, all are proud of being Jews. The commonly mentioned "Jewish characteristics" can be explained in a large measure by conditions of economic and social life under which the Jew has been constrained to live for generations in every country.

Although the Jews have religious expression ranging from the extreme of orthodoxy to the extreme of liberalism, there are fewer internal conflicts than in most religions, for Judaism is not so much a dogma as it is a progressive education. Jewish children are eager pupils, not because they are naturally brighter than others, but because the whole Jewish life develops mental alertness and the learned are traditionally respected. The religious forms are highly organized and of great historical as well as contemporary interest. Every teacher should learn the significance of the 14 holidays that occur during the school year. Some effort should be made to understand what the Talmud deals with.

Linguistically the Jews are among the best equipped people in the world. They know Hebrew for religious purposes, Yiddish for common use, and the language or the languages of the country in which they live for commercial purposes. Most Hungarian Jews speak Hungarian and German, and Slovak if from the north, Roumanian if from the east; and Croatian if from the south. Some good books are: "The Promised Land," by Mary Antin, published by the Houghton Mifflin Company; "Jewish Life in Modern Times," by Cohen, published by Dodd, Mead & Company; "The Jews in America," by Peters, published by the John C. Winston Co.; "Jewish Ceremonial Institutions and Customs," by Rosenau, published by the Friedenwald Co., Baltimore; "The Talmud," by Darmstetter, published by the Jewish Publication Society, Philadelphia.

HUNGARIANS

Hungarians should properly be called Magyars, but they themselves have no objection to the name which is derived from the geographical district in which something over 50 per cent of non-Magyars live. As a people they have come into national consciousness in comparatively recent times. Their nearly successful struggle for independence from the Germans has given them confidence. Their anti-German feeling has been strong and their disdain for other peoples has been striking. The result is that a large proportion of them know no language but Magyar, while many Slovaks and Roumanians know equally well their own language, German, and Magyar. The Hungarians have strong Protestant denominations, a large number of Roman Catholics, and not a few Greek Catholics. A book full of information but unsympathetic with the Magyars is "Racial Problems in Hungary," by Scotus Viator.

ITALIANS

Most of the Italians in Cleveland, as in the United States, come from southern Italy, following the line of their commerce. From northern Italy they follow their ship lines to South America. There are divisions among the people according to the provinces from which they come. Each province has a somewhat distinctive dialect, but since all official business is in good Italian, the people understand it even if they do not speak it. The large majority of the Italians have Catholic traditions, but both in Italy and in America show only moderate devotion to the church. Although there are two large Italian congregations in Cleveland, it has not been possible to establish a parochial school. There is no language richer than Italian in form or literary content, and no history, ancient or modern, more full of heroic incidents and high ideals.

LITHUANIANS

Although there are many Lithuanians in America, they are very little known. Living in the midst of Russian Poland, they are generally thought to be Slavs, but as a matter of fact they are a quite distinct nationality which for many generations has preserved its language and many of its traditions, while adopting much from its Polish environment. Like the Poles, the Lithuanians are Catholics, but since they identify the church with the Polish imposition of culture, they are inclined to be lukewarm religiously or to go into anti-church organizations. In fact they are often less hostile to the Russians, who lay political restrictions on them, than to the Poles, who seek to make their culture dominant. Within the past 10 years there has been a remarkable revival of a nationalism which had hitherto seemed almost dead. There are now several Lithuanian newspapers in America, many of whose subscribers have had to learn to read Lithuanian since coming here.

POLES

Poland, divided into three subject provinces by Germany, Russia, and Austria, is fired by the one ideal of national freedom. The Prussian attempt to Germanize her province is the finest illustration that society affords of the impossibility of coercive assimilation. The tremendous emotionalism nourished by this Polish consciousness has made them highly idealistic. It is next to impossible for the children to feel the controlling emotions of their parents and no substitute has been provided to take its place. Their rebellion against authority is illustrated by the frequent secessions of Poles from the Roman Catholic Church. They secede and establish independent congregations which they call the Polish Catholic Church. There was formerly such a congregation on the southeast side, and within the past year one has been established in the old Olney Art Museum on West 14th Street.

Poland has given the world several literary and musical persons of great eminence. However, the problem of the Pole is one of the most difficult which America has to solve, though conditions are better in Cleveland than in most other cities. Much help can be secured by co-operating with the positive qualities which they possess.

RUSSIANS AND RUTHENIANS

These have already been discussed. They belong to the newer immigration. The Ruthenians are the only Slavs who are anti-Russian. This is because they are generally Greek Catholic and have been made to feel that the Orthodox Church will be imposed on them if Russia is in control. Formerly Galicia, from which they came, was part of Russia and Orthodox, but when it came into the possession of Austria the existence of congregations of the Orthodox Greek Church in large numbers was thought to be dangerous to the government. The result was that the Roman Church, in return for their acknowledgment of the headship of the Pope, allowed them to retain intact their Orthodox ritual and their married clergy. This was the origin of the Greek Catholic or Uniate Church. The church interior and the service are hardly distinguishable from the Orthodox Church, yet allegiance is to the Roman Catholic Church. This makes a complex situation which cannot fail to have interesting developments in the future.

ROUMANIANS

No large group of immigrants is less known than the Roumanians, who have come to America in very recent years. They have come almost exclusively from Austria-Hungary, and like the Ruthenians belong to the Orthodox and Greek Catholic churches. There is a strong tendency to organize along national lines. At the recent dedication of a Roumanian church on Buckeye Road the tenor of the priest's remarks was that they should drop the use of Magyar, which many know better than Roumanian, and maintain the integrity of the Roumanian ideas. The Roumanians claim to be descendants of the Romans, who colonized their region and their language has a large proportion of Latin roots. Nevertheless their sympathies are prevailingly Slavic.

SLOVAKS

As has been said above, the Slovaks are linguistically closely related to the Bohemians, but unlike them they have never known political freedom. They have had less contact with the modern currents of the world, and have thus preserved more of the old customs and traditions. They have little literature of their own, but several of their writers have written in Bohemian. They come from Northern Hungary, and the effort to Magyarize them, which has been constant and especially severe in recent years and which is the cause of the large immigration, has resulted in great bitterness and increasing devotion to their language.

SLOVENIANS

The Slovenians or "Griners" come from southern Austria where they had been almost Germanized. They have come in large numbers to Cleveland in the last 15 years. They have been highly illiterate and are almost all Catholics. The clergy in Austria is prevailingly in favor with the government and has kept down rather than stimulated national feeling. Here in America, however, there is a growing feeling for the right of national freedom in Europe.

OTHER NATIONALITIES

It is unnecessary to discuss in detail the other nationalities represented in our public schools. There are some facts common to all these which have been described, the most striking of which is the great number of mutual benefit societies, all of which have a certain social and national value. For example, the Slovenians have 72 such societies. Some are for men alone, some are for women alone, and some for men and women. In the National Bohemian Hall on Broadway, 68 societies, clubs, and lodges meet every month. The Jews have at least 150 Vereins, as well as more comprehensive organizations, such as the Hebrew Relief and Socialist and Zionist clubs. The same thing runs through every nationality.

70

The object of the teacher should be to see her group from the inside as it sees itself. In this way not only will sympathetic relations be established, but human values recognized which cannot be comprehended when seen from the outside. Dr. Edward A. Steiner's books, while perhaps glorifying the immigrant overmuch, will be of great value in arousing respect.

Summary

The success of the teacher in dealing with foreign children depends in no small measure on her personal relations with them. In order that the most effective work may be done, it is essential that the teacher should know something of the history and characteristics of the different national groups. The object of this chapter is to present in brief outline some of the more significant facts concerning each one of the leading nationalities, and to give in addition references to the most reliable and interesting books concerning them.

CHAPTER V

THE PROBLEM OF EDUCATION FOR THE FOREIGN CHILDREN

The problem of educating children of recent foreign origin divides itself into two major phases and almost innumerable minor ones. The two main divisions of the problem have to do respectively with education for the recently arrived non-English-speaking children; and with the far greater number of children scattered throughout the school system who come from homes where English is not spoken but who have themselves acquired some facility in the use of the language and some familiarity with American customs and standards.

STEAMER CLASSES

Fifteen years ago, in 1901, the Cleveland school system first recognized the necessity of making special provision for teaching English to recently arrived immigrant children. In that year the principal of Harmon School organized the first class for non-English-speaking children and termed it a "Steamer Class" because it was made up of pupils who had come to Cleveland directly from the steamer which brought them to this country. The name has persisted and ever since that day the special classes for non-English-speaking children in the day schools have been known as steamer classes.

The value of this educational innovation soon became apparent. Children who cannot speak English are misfits in the regular grades. They must be given an opportunity to learn the language before they are placed in a class of 40 or more other children and expected to carry on regular grade work. Unfortunately, the steamer class cannot become a very effective instrument for assisting recently arrived immigrant children until further provisions are made for transporting such children to these special classes whenever they happen to enroll in schools where provision for teaching them has not been made.

Under the present arrangements steamer classes are organized in the schools that regularly receive large numbers of new immigrants. Here they meet an important need, but they do not help the pupil whose parents have found a place to live a little removed from the other recent arrivals and so have sent their children to a school where there are not enough foreign children in attendance to warrant the establishment of special classes. This is one of the problems which the school system has never satisfactorily solved.

At the present time such cases are often handled in a most unsatisfactory manner. The non-English-speaking child cannot keep up with his companions in the regular grades. For this reason he is sent to a special class, but if there is no steamer class available, the pupil is all too frequently assigned to the backward class. This is not because the backward class is the right place for him, but rather because it furnishes an easy means of disposing of a pupil who, through no fault of his own, is an unsatisfactory member of a regular grade, holds back the other pupils, and makes the teacher's work more difficult and less effective.

Attention has already been directed to some of these problems in the report of the Survey entitled "Schools and Classes for Exceptional Children." That report discusses cases in which mentally deficient children are assigned to foreign classes, and normal foreign children to classes for backward pupils because the school organization has not been sufficiently flexible and sufficiently discriminating to examine each child carefully, diagnose his case accurately, and then see to it that he is assigned to a class which will give him the particular sort of instruction he needs and that he is transported to such a class if one is not available in his own building.

The truth is that the problem of teaching foreign children to speak English has never been regarded by the public schools as one of their serious problems. Although classes for these children have been in existence for the past 15 years, it is only during the past two years that the statistical summaries of the annual school reports have shown the number of pupils and teachers in them. Moreover, during the entire period of 15 years the work of these classes has never been of sufficient importance to receive mention in the annual reports of the superintendent and board.

The data that are available indicate that in 1913 there were 15 classes with more than 400 children enrolled. In 1914 and 1915 the number of classes was about 25 and the number of pupils a little over 700. Toward the close of 1915 these figures were very much reduced because the European war resulted in largely cutting off the stream of immigration to this country. The effects of the war were still more fully felt in 1916 so that in the spring of that year almost all the steamer classes had been suspended.

The educational officers of the city have never

worked out any special methods for teaching English to these non-English-speaking children. There is no special supervision of the work and no provision in the Normal School for training teachers to do it. As a result the classes are far less efficient than they should be. There is a special educational technique for teaching a new language which is far different in its methods from that employed in teaching subject matter to pupils in their own language. This has been amply demonstrated in the special classes of several of our cities, notably New York and Boston, and still more strikingly illustrated in the schools of Porto Rico and the Philippines, in which hundreds of thousands of children are taught the English language so effectively that they successfully carry on their entire school work in it after a remarkably short period of special teaching.

The school systems of these insular possessions have developed methods of language teaching incomparably more effective than those in use in our American school systems and vastly more efficient than any commonly employed in our high schools or colleges. In the lesson of their experience the fact which stands out with most impressive clearness is that the problem of teaching children a new language is one of great difficulty when attempted by traditional school methods and one of remarkable ease and celerity when the proper special methods are employed.

In view of the great importance of English teaching in the schools of Cleveland, the Board of Education ought to take vigorous steps to increase the efficiency of this work. Two steps are urgently needed. The first is to secure a supervisor thoroughly conversant with the most effective methods of teaching English to non-English-speaking children. Through the services of such a supervisor a trained corps of teachers could soon be developed.

The second important step is to provide the administrative readjustments necessary to put every non-English-speaking child into a special class, even if this involves transportation from one district to another. In this connection special care should be taken to avoid assigning foreign children of normal mentality to backward classes or backward English-speaking children to foreign classes.

ENGLISH-SPEAKING CHILDREN FROM NON-ENGLISH-SPEAKING HOMES

It has already been shown that more than half of the children in the schools of Cleveland come from non-English-speaking homes. A study of

the figures showing how these children are dis-
tributed through the different grades and among
the various schools leads to the conclusion that
the only uniform condition permeating the
entire situation is the universal heterogeniety
of the school population. There are very few
schools indeed having anything approaching a
homogeneous student body. In every school
there are children from non-English-speaking
families, and in most of them these children are
divided among a large number of nationalities.
Moreover, some schools have large numbers of
foreign children in the upper grades while in
others they are mainly in the lower ones. In
some schools one nationality predominates
among the older children and another among
the younger ones. The school population is a
synthesis of the most varied elements. Tables
5 and 6 are introduced to show the numbers of
children of the more important nationality
groups in the different schools from which data
were gathered by the Survey.

A study of Table 5 reveals conditions that are
not only interesting, but constitute a very puz-
zling educational problem. The data were
gathered from 98 elementary schools. In a
majority of cases the children from non-English-
speaking homes outnumber those from English-
speaking homes. It would thus seem on first
78

TABLE 5.—CHILDREN IN LEADING NATIONALITY GROUPS IN EACH ELEMENTARY SCHOOL ON BASIS OF THE LANGUAGE OF THE HOME

School	English	German	Yiddish	Bohemian	Italian	Hungarian	Polish	Slovak	Other foreign	Total
Addison	508	24	..	1	..	7	..	..	7	547
Alabama	42	65	6	1	2	3	94	2	91	306
Barkwill	139	15	..	359	..	..	10	..	..	523
Bolton	910	82	8	45	2	3	..	1	60	1,111
Boulevard	361	84	..	39	..	27	3	14	9	537
Broadway	436	33	..	15	2	3	258	..	68	815
Brownell	248	11	8	1	650	1	1	6	38	964
Buhrer	491	110	..	3	10	5	3	7	9	638
Case	220	252	..	..	3	20	44	46	165	750
Case-Woodland	100	39	448	132	15	47	10	24	22	837
Central	363	27	440	..	5	16	3	..	29	883
Chesterfield	438	9	..	2	12	..	..	..	1	462
Clark	342	162	..	198	..	22	..	20	6	750
Columbia	1,043	28	10	..	5	2	..	..	6	1,094
Corlett	93	9	..	191	5	14	12	6	..	330
Dawning	318	368	..	81	7	37	7	18	24	860
Denison	895	85	..	11	6	2	2	3	84	1,088
Detroit	508	85	1	3	12	28	1	1	82	721
Dike	277	58	659	3	..	15	2	..	49	1,063
Doan	787	4	..	..	..	..	..	..	4	795
Dunham	672	59	7	..	2	6	1	..	18	765
Eagle	26	6	2	2	88	13	23	116	380	656
East Boulevard	349	76	1	126	122	44	..	5	19	742
East Clark	306	23	..	1	13	5	..	..	59	407
East Denison	389	80	..	18	..	24	100	1	9	621
East Madison	487	164	1	6	3	8	15	39	260	983
Empire	567	93	1	1	1	3	9	1	25	701
Fairmount	400	6	1	..	192	1	..	..	3	603
Fowler	282	56	..	248	2	10	24	12	3	637
Fruitland	266	26	..	..	..	2	2	..	14	310
Fullerton	10	17	..	67	..	..	684	..	2	780
Giddings	402	84	158	74	4	24	16	..	85	847
Gilbert	405	294	..	260	3	84	5	26	11	1,088
Gordon	414	128	..	7	3	15	..	2	19	588
Halle	558	152	4	4	5	6	..	4	13	746
Harmon	34	4	31	1	542	..	2	4	59	677
Harvard	218	33	..	38	2	..	415	3	5	714
Hazeldell	936	101	4	..	4	1	..	..	22	1,068
Hicks	294	102	4	2	5	472	36	114	42	1,071
Hodge	508	205	4	4	4	10	24	7	75	841
Hough	782	37	4	1	3	5	1	1	7	841
Huck	169	114	..	166	2	..	18	..	2	471
Kennard	162	33	847	1	63	..	17	2	71	1,196
Kentucky	367	51	1	1	5	90	6	2	66	589
Kinsman	543	200	11	12	6	247	15	49	95	1,178
Landon	692	87	..	4	..	2	2	7	16	810
Lawn	374	61	..	1	5	11	..	..	10	462
Lincoln	299	66	12	133	3	321	..	8	22	864
Longwood	131	7	427	8	47	19	3	3	6	651
Marion	149	7	132	..	271	7	14	80	63	723

TABLE 5.—(*Continued*)

School	English	German	Yiddish	Bohemian	Italian	Hungarian	Polish	Slovak	Other foreign	Total
Mayflower	127	34	494	34	184	28	42	98	136	1,177
Memorial	300	130	..	2	15	33	75	6	336	897
Memphis	415	67	..	12	1	16	1	2	9	523
Miles	380	32	..	122	2	2	22	1	12	573
Miles Park	488	49	..	49	37	1	28	35	13	700
Milford	389	391	..	304	5	51	2	47	4	1,193
Mill	342	151	8	3	3	5	4	..	5	521
Moulton	189	53	..	4	16	5	20	..	14	301
Mound	91	34	..	183	.	1	256	..	1	566
Mt. Pleasant	334	39	6	126	18	2	2	5	11	543
Murray Hill	171	1	..	..	1,171	..	..	..	5	1,348
North Doan	612	40	9	2	2	3	..	..	20	688
Nottingham	342	99	2	3	25	28	3	..	70	572
Observation	166	15	1	10	98	..	..	..	9	299
Orchard	539	205	4	5	2	171	2	13	39	980
Outhwaite	245	58	1,033	1	8	50	9	3	33	1,440
Parkwood	582	6	..	..	4	1	..	..	..	593
Pearl	170	49	..	17	2	..	38	..	5	281
Quincy	418	84	10	138	6	23	7	7	24	717
Rawlings	62	61	2	4	..	537	21	16	21	724
Rice	227	68	5	347	27	294	5	66	21	1,060
Rockwell	92	5	2	..	..	2	2	..	23	126
Rosedale	750	33	..	..	25	..	..	..	9	817
Sackett	692	195	..	225	26	17	5	7	6	1,173
St. Clair	359	163	3	5	10	16	109	7	90	762
Scranton	446	167	1	7	2	22	11	43	25	724
Sibley	624	41	147	6	20	7	..	1	57	903
South	478	43	1	4	218	4	..	..	158	906
South Case	247	15	638	..	50	8	..	..	2	960
Sowinski	502	127	10	..	3	..	185	..	65	892
Stanard	235	133	6	1	2	8	5	5	280	675
Sterling	481	21	60	..	114	1	..	3	42	722
Todd	265	83	1	46	3	13	45	5	6	467
Tremont	276	202	4	10	22	20	483	266	495	1,778
Union	275	55	1	440	..	1	103	28	31	934
Wade Park	653	40	..	..	2	..	1	..	23	719
Walton	382	219	1	56	66	22	1	20	8	775
Warner	335	50	..	37	40	1	..	..	8	471
Waring	357	165	1	..	3	15	21	..	50	612
Warren	250	110	1	438	..	8	87	55	12	961
Washington Pk.	110	11	..	131	..	..	20	..	4	276
Watterson	356	44	..	..	101	4	..	..	19	524
Waverly	381	48	3	1	2	7	..	1	48	491
Willard	839	235	3	16	8	19	3	4	27	1,154
Willson	682	75	1	2	3	9	1	..	21	794
Woodland	218	63	2	59	5	504	5	97	66	1,019
Woodland Hills	393	96	..	185	2	8	9	80	27	800
Wooldridge	477	91	527	19	4	37	8	3	45	1,211
	37,454	8,118	6,219	5,325	4,493	3,686	3,523	1,558	4,670	75,046

consideration that it would be a comparatively simple matter to modify the instruction given in each school so as to meet most adequately the needs of the pupils. In point of fact this is rendered exceedingly difficult by the complex character of the group from non-English-speaking homes.

TABLE 6.—CHILDREN IN LEADING NATIONALITY GROUPS IN EACH HIGH SCHOOL ON BASIS OF THE LANGUAGE OF THE HOME

School	English	German	Yiddish	Bohe-mian	Italian	Hunga-rian	Polish	Slovak	Other foreign	Total
Central	542	151	364	23	39	36	9	3	76	1,243
Collinwood	71	1	..	..	1	..	..	..	3	76
East Commerce	491	130	66	38	5	23	10	3	78	844
East High	1,070	49	2	4	16	2	9	..	16	1,168
East Technical	1,178	376	139	164	40	30	32	17	110	2,086
Glenville	817	51	4	..	1	4	..	..	13	890
Lincoln	386	75	1	14	2	2	7	11	16	514
South	431	60	..	107	2	..	42	5	25	672
West High	576	20	..	..	..	1	..	1	3	601
West Technical	763	180	..	24	2	4	4	..	17	994
Total	6,325	1,093	576	374	108	102	113	40	357	9,088

In the city as a whole the only homogeneous element in the different school populations is the group of children from English-speaking homes. They do not constitute a majority of all the children, but, except in a few cases, they constitute a larger group than any other single group. In the entire city there are 26 schools in which there is a group of one nationality outnumbering the children from English-speaking homes, but in most cases these children do not constitute a majority of the children enrolled in the school.

In only 11 schools are there homogeneous foreign groups so numerous as to constitute more than half of the children enrolled. Six of these schools have groups of children from Yiddish-speaking homes so large as to constitute a majority of the whole school enrollment; in two cases the Polish children are in the majority; in two cases the Italians; and in one case the Hungarians.

Such facts as these, together with the data of Table 5, indicate the great difficulties involved in attempting to modify instruction to meet the special needs of special national groups. In a single classroom there may be pupils of a dozen different nationalities. In most of the classrooms of the city the largest single group is made up of children from English-speaking homes. In only a few cases are there classes in which practically all the children are of the same nationality.

Nevertheless the very complexity of the problem points the way with some definiteness to certain wise courses of educational procedure. It is entirely certain that in a city in which a majority of the children are from non-English-speaking homes a definite and conscious effort should be made by the school authorities to acquire an intelligent understanding of the national origins, traditions, histories, and aspirations of the more important immigrant groups. Teachers and principals should cultivate a more intelligent and sympathetic understanding of the home problems and conditions of these children.

In addition to these general considerations, there are certain definite and specific courses of action which are indicated by the conditions that have been discussed. It is apparent that the most important subject in the schools of Cleveland is English. This would probably remain true if there were no foreign children enrolled, but under the present conditions it is doubly true. The one educational certainty is that the ability to read, write, and speak the English language easily and correctly is the ability which will conduce most effectively to the moral welfare, the cultural development, the vocational prosperity, and the individual happiness of this great mass of children now in the public schools of this city.

SUMMARY

The problem of educating immigrant children has two major phases: teaching them English, and teaching them after they have learned English. For the purpose of teaching them English, Cleveland began 15 years ago the establishment of steamer classes, which increased in number until in the past year they enrolled some 700 children in 25 classes.

These classes are valuable and fairly effective. Provisions should be made for transferring non-English-speaking children to them when such children enroll in schools where steamer classes have not been organized. The work could be rendered much more effective by adopting methods of English teaching such as have been developed in New York and Boston, or the superior methods in use in Porto Rico and the Philippine Islands.

The problems of furnishing the best schooling for the foreign children after they have learned to speak English are rendered difficult by the large numbers of national groups and the complex manner in which they are scattered through the schools all over the city. The one educational certainty is that the most important single educational asset that the schools could give all the children, whether they come from English-speaking or non-English-speaking homes, would be a mastery of speaking, reading, and writing the English language.

CHAPTER VI

THE ADULT IMMIGRANT AND THE SCHOOL

The most important instrumentality for the instruction of the adult immigrant is the public night school. Cleveland has maintained night schools for the past 35 years. The first one was probably established in 1880 and had as its object the instruction of boys and young men who had left school early or had not been so fortunate as to receive any regular education whatever. This first school was supported partly by the Newsboys' and Bootblacks' Home and partly by the Board of Education. Its work proved so successful that the Board took over its control and proceeded to establish other similar schools elsewhere in the city. Very soon the character of the work carried on began to change. More and more non-English-speaking men attended until finally the evening schools have become almost exclusively devoted to the instruction of foreigners in the English language.

EVENING SCHOOLS FOR ADULT FOREIGNERS

The evening schools in Cleveland have increased in scope and importance until they have become a large educational enterprise, enrolling in the school year of 1914–15 more than 11,000 students.

These schools open in October and continue in session for 20 or 22 weeks, being open four nights each week. At the close of the regular term in March most of them suspend work, but a few are continued for a further period of several weeks. The experiment has even been tried of continuing a few of the night schools through the summer months. The classes are held in regular elementary school buildings and about one-fourth of the teachers are also employed as teachers in the day schools while the remaining three-fourths are people working at other occupations during the day.

The following data give the principal facts concerning the Cleveland evening elementary schools for 1914–15.

Total number of classes	132
Total number of pupils registered	11,383
Range of ages	15 to 60
Average age	23
Number of nights in winter session	102
Number of buildings in use	34
Number of men teachers	89
Number of women teachers	43
Total number of teachers	132
Teachers also employed in day schools	34
Wages of teachers per evening	$2.00 to $2.50
Total enrollment, male	9,082
Total enrollment, female	2,301
Total enrollment, both sexes	11,383
Average attendance, male	3,087
Average attendance, female	796
Average attendance, both sexes	3,883
Salaries of teachers in 1914–15	$25,577
Wages of custodians in 1914–15	$5,626
Contingent expenses in 1914–15	$76
Total cost of instruction in 1914–15	$31,279

Among the students attending these classes, 26 out of every 27 are foreigners. The cosmopolitan nature of the student body is shown by the figures of Table 7, which gives the number of students in each of 45 nationalities enrolled during the school year of 1914–15. It will be noted that the total of this table is 11,402, although the official records show a total enrollment of 11,383. The Survey has not been able to find the cause of this slight discrepancy as both sets of figures are from the official records.

CITIZENSHIP CLASSES

In addition to their regular work, the evening schools established, two years ago, classes in citizenship for the benefit of aliens desiring to secure naturalization papers. During that winter these classes enrolled more than 1,400 men. Last year the total enrollment was about 1,300. During the winter of 1915–16 the number was less than 600. This does not mean, however, that during the past winter 600 men have been in regular attendance at these classes. This number represents the total enrollment for the school year, that is, the number of different individuals who have joined the classes and been in attendance for any amount of time, long or short. During the winter of 1915–16 the citizen-

TABLE 7.—NATIONALITIES OF EVENING SCHOOL STUDENTS
IN CLEVELAND IN 1915

Nationality	Number
Magyar	1,964
Hebrew, Russian	1,497
Austrian	1,259
Polish	982
Italian (south)	762
Bohemian	632
Slovenian	428
Slovak	351
American, white	349
Lithuanian	318
German	300
Syrian	274
Russian	266
Italian (north)	260
Croatian	252
Greek	235
Hebrew, Polish	218
Hebrew, other foreign	185
Finnish	143
Armenian	90
Roumanian	87
American negro	77
Bulgarian	67
English	54
Hebrew, German	50
Swedish	43
Dutch	40
Ruthenian	31
Irish	28
Norwegian	27
Hebrew, Roumanian	26
Serbian	20
Danish	16
Swiss	12
Macedonian	11
Turkish	9
Canadian, English	7
Canadian, French	6
French	6
Scotch	6
Spanish American	4
Japanese	3
Moravian	3
Chinese	2
Welsh	2
Total	11,402

ship classes were in session one night each week and the attendance, which began with 230 in October, rose to nearly 300 two weeks later and then slowly but steadily declined to a little over 100 at the close of March.

The motives which prompted the establishment of the citizenship classes are deserving of the heartiest approbation and support. Socially and educationally this innovation is wisely planned and worthy of continuation and extension. Nevertheless the fact is that these classes are making a most meager contribution toward helping aliens to become American citizens. Their enrollment is progressively decreasing and their attendance is but a small fraction of their enrollment. The official records indicate that the great majority of the men who enter these classes become discouraged and drop out after attending for a few nights. It is undoubtedly true that the great European war has stemmed the tide of immigration and taken from the city many who might otherwise have been in attendance at these classes. Nevertheless this cannot be the true explanation of the shrinking enrollment and small attendance.

During the early months of 1916 there were from 100 to 200 men in attendance in the citizenship classes. At the same time the number of adult foreigners of voting age in Cleveland who had not even taken out their first papers was probably not less than 50,000. Moreover, the number of unnaturalized aliens in the city has been steadily and rapidly increasing for a number of years and has now reached the point where Cleveland's record in this matter is poorer than that of almost any other large city.

Under these circumstances it is a matter calling for serious concern that the citizenship classes should be shrinking in size, that most of their students drop after a few nights of attendance, that the official records of the work fail to indicate how many of the students who take the course succeed in securing their naturalization papers, and that the attendance amounts to less than one-half of one per cent of the men in the city to whom such classes should make their strongest appeal.

In the opinion of the members of the Survey Staff the causes of these unsatisfactory conditions are to be found in the character of the instruction given in these classes. The trouble is that the teaching does not follow any well matured plan and is not skilfully done. It suffers from the same sorts of weaknesses that restrict the value of the instruction given in the regular evening schools. The nature of these shortcomings is considered in detail in the following section.

QUALITY OF INSTRUCTION IN EVENING SCHOOLS
It appears that the educational officials of the
Cleveland school system are highly satisfied
with the quality of the work done in the evening
elementary schools. In the printed report for
1914, and again in that for 1915, the city superintendent and the supervisor of evening schools
inform the public that "Our evening schools
rank high as to quality and amount of work
done, and are very much superior to nearly all
of those in other cities in regularity of attendance and much lower in cost per capita."

It is impossible for the members of the Survey
Staff to share the optimism of the superintendent and supervisor in this matter. During
the course of the Survey 66 visits have been
made by five members of the Survey Staff to
evening elementary classes. As a result the conclusion has been forced upon these observers
that the work done in these classes is very far
from ranking high in either quality or amount.
While there are many enthusiastic teachers and
hundreds of eagerly conscientious pupils, the
classroom work exhibits an almost total lack
of unified plan, matured method, and intelligent
direction. The trouble is that the teaching
methods have not been intelligently adapted to
the needs and abilities of the pupils.

The typical characteristics of the work are

well illustrated by that observed in five successive classrooms in one school visited in March, 1916. The pupils were almost entirely young foreign men of from 25 to 30 years of age. Many of them were employed in one of Cleveland's great steel manufacturing establishments. They were not illiterate, but they had almost no knowledge of English. They were all weary from their day's work and they kept awake only by the exercise of apparent effort.

In the first of the five classes a writing lesson was being conducted, and these husky laboring men were busily engaged in copying, "I am a yellow bird. I can sing. I can fly. I can sing to you."

In the second class the teacher was barely able to talk English and the work was almost entirely conducted by the translation method. The teacher made several fruitless attempts to get the pupils to speak English. He did this by telling them repeatedly, "Think the sentence in your own language and then try to translate it into English." After this had failed to produce satisfactory results, the teacher gave it up and had them read a selection about making pickles from cucumbers.

The third class was taught by a bright young foreigner who had apparently received a classical education. The work was conducted just as are many classes in Latin. The teacher spoke English almost perfectly, and although his pupils could neither speak nor understand it, he carefully explained to them about inflections, voices, moods, tenses, numbers, and persons. He then told them they that were to conjugate "to have" and "to be." After this was explained to them in their own language, the pupils all went to the board and began to write "I have, thou hast, he has," and "I am, thou art, he is," etc. The teacher explained that "art" was the second person singular, indicative mood, present tense, of the substantive verb "be." After this the class had a reading lesson from the third reader about a robin that said, "God loves the flowers and birds too much to send the cold to freeze them."

In the fourth room the pupils had a reading lesson about "Little drops of water, Little grains of sand." They then had a spelling lesson of the words in the reading selection. The teacher was interested, vivacious, and expended a great amount of nervous energy in talking very rapidly and almost incessantly. She took up most of the time with her own activity and most of the pupils could not understand what she was talking about.

In the fifth and last class the teacher was also most voluble and talked more than all the stu-

dents combined. It was a reading lesson and the
14 men present were engaged in reading a selection beginning

"Oh, baby, dear baby,
Whatever you do,
You are king of the home
And we all bend to you."

Similar examples might be multiplied from the
written records of the work observed in the
evening classes, and classes of the sort described
may be seen by any one who will take the time
to visit the evening schools of the city. Perhaps
the most impressive characteristic of it all is
that every teacher appears to be entirely free
to teach whatever he pleases by any methods
that he wishes to use. The lessons assigned and
the methods employed in the different rooms
are astonishingly varied. There seems to be no
effective supervision, no plan for improving the
teachers in service, and no effort to find out
which of the many methods used produces the
best results.

REORGANIZATION ESSENTIAL

In the opinion of the Survey Staff it is essential
that the evening elementary school work of
Cleveland be reorganized. Some of the results
of the work as at present conducted are revealed
by the attendance records. The data for the 22

weeks of the regular term of 1915–16 are shown in Table 8 and Diagram 7. They refer to the evening elementary schools and the citizenship classes. They show that when the classes opened in October, some 2,800 students enrolled and almost all were actually in attendance. A month later the enrollment had increased by 2,500, but the attendance was only 500 greater than at the beginning. This means that even in the first few lessons large numbers of the students had become discouraged and dropped out.

From this point on the enrollment steadily increased, showing that new pupils were continually joining the classes, but the number belonging and the number in actual attendance steadily decreased, indicating that other pupils were dropping out. By the end of the regular term in March, the enrollment was more than 7,000, while the attendance was only a little over 1,000.

Moreover, there is evidence pointing to the probability that the loose methods of record keeping used in this part of the school work result in reporting conditions somewhat more favorably than the facts warrant. Under the present regulations a class is suspended when the attendance falls below 15. Upon the occasions of visits to the classes the pupils present were counted by the Survey visitors and in a

95

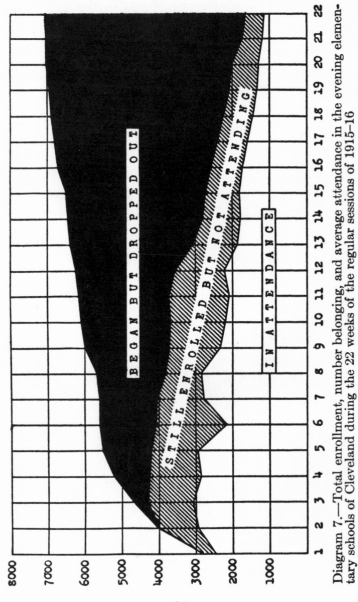

Diagram 7.—Total enrollment, number belonging, and average attendance in the evening elementary schools of Cleveland during the 22 weeks of the regular sessions of 1915-16

96

large number of cases fewer than 15 were found present on the night of the visit, although the number reported at the central office as the average for that week was always 15 or over.

TABLE 8.—TOTAL ENROLLMENT, NUMBER BELONGING, AND AVERAGE ATTENDANCE IN THE EVENING ELEMENTARY SCHOOLS OF CLEVELAND DURING THE 22 WEEKS OF THE REGULAR SESSIONS OF 1915–16

Week ending	Total enrollment	Belonging	Attendance
October 14	2,834	2,831	2,487
" 21	4,044	4,001	2,947
" 28	4,694	4,314	3,122
November 4	5,233	4,276	2,908
" 11	5,545	4,223	2,971
" 17	5,655	4,074	2,157
" 24	5,655	4,069	2,817
December 3	5,700	3,818	2,868
" 9	6,001	3,723	2,391
" 17	6,115	3,690	2,210
" 23	6,188	3,766	2,108
January 6	6,252	3,586	2,231
" 13	6,399	3,076	1,881
" 20	6,458	2,818	1,780
" 27	6,515	2,739	1,813
February 4	6,746	2,610	1,742
" 10	6,810	2,423	1,614
" 17	6,910	2,239	1,461
" 24	6,960	2,091	1,360
March 3	7,040	2,031	1,331
" 9	7,043	1,735	1,203
" 16	7,048	1,673	1,191

These discrepancies would be possible on the supposition that the visitor almost always happened to call on a night when the attendance was lower than it was for the three other evenings of that week. However, it seems more probable that the record keeping is not entirely accurate. The following comparison shows for

7

the first 10 classes in the list compiled by the Survey the number counted on the evening of the visit and the number reported for that class on the official record as being the average attendance for that week.

Count	Official report
14	15
19	19
11	15
12	15
10	15
8	16
32	32
18	25
16	24
21	21

Whatever the facts may be with regard to the accuracy of the reports, the important features of the situation are that the attendance in the night classes is very much less than the enrollment and that great numbers of immigrants enter the classes, become discouraged, and drop out after a brief attendance. Cleveland has been repeatedly told that there were more than 10,000 students enrolled in the night schools. Probably few citizens have realized that this number represented, not students in school, but rather names in books. They have not realized that a count of all the students actually present on any pleasant evening during the middle of the term would have shown only about one-third of that number and that a count near the close of the term would have shown one-fifth or less.

The tragic part of the situation is that every year thousands of earnest and hopeful foreigners flock to the night schools in keen anticipation of learning English, and after a few weeks become discouraged and drop out because the teachers do not meet their needs. Since they cannot understand what is going on, their interest flags. As the weeks pass by, physical weariness overcomes them more and more each night. Finally they sink into despondency and discouragement as they see their cherished dream of mastering the new language depart. This is no matter of casual import for these men and women. They are not children and most of them are not students. Concentrating their minds on the lesson implies painful effort. If this intense application does not bring them within a few weeks some results that the immigrant can appreciate he begins to realize that his constructive ideal, his dream of becoming an American, his opportunity for success in the new land, are not to be attained through the public school.

These men and women of the evening schools have no abstract zeal for knowledge. They are interested in the immediate, the concrete, and the practical. They resemble children in that they are ignorant and need help, but they are mature in ideas and realizations and keenly conscious of specific needs. This is why they cannot be interested in inflections and tenses and why they are not gripped or thrilled by reading about the beautiful posies and the pretty birdies. They want to learn to talk English, and they can be kept interested only so long as they can use each day what they learned the night before.

There are 70,000 people in Cleveland who cannot speak English, and there are few social, civic, or educational problems more important than to make it possible for this tenth of the city's population to understand and communicate with the other nine-tenths. The number of unnaturalized adult foreign men is nearly as large as that of the non-English-speaking inhabitants. Moreover these conditions are becoming worse rapidly and steadily. Again Cleveland makes a poorer showing in these respects than any other large city.

For these reasons the Survey deems it essential that the elementary evening schools of this city should be reorganized so as to do efficient work in teaching English to foreigners. What is most needed is leadership. One thoroughly competent supervisor, charged with responsibility for making the work efficient, and given greatly increased power in the selection, training, and direction of his assistants, could work a rapid reform in the whole situation. While increased appropriations are needed for supplies and for teachers, they are not nearly so important as skilled and enterprising leadership. Cleveland should profit by the example of other cities. The school authorities here should know what Detroit has accomplished within the past year in dealing with this same problem. Board members and educational officials should carefully read the report entitled, "The School and the Immigrant," recently published by the New York Department of Education. A careful examination should be made of the 20 different books and sets of books telling how to teach English most successfully to foreigners. The city cannot afford to be indifferent, or inefficient, or contented in its attitude toward helping its aliens to help themselves.

SUMMARY

The evening elementary schools of Cleveland have been in existence for 35 years. At the present time their total enrollment each year is in the neighborhood of 10,000. The classes are open during about 20 weeks, four nights a week. Almost all the students are foreigners and their main object is to learn English. In addition to their regular work the evening schools have established classes in citizenship.

In the opinion of the Survey Staff, based on visits to a considerable proportion of the classes, the work in the evening elementary schools falls far short of being well and efficiently conducted. The records of attendance show that only a small proportion of those who enroll remain more than a few weeks. Many thousands begin, become discouraged, and drop out. It is the conviction of the members of the Survey Staff that a reorganization of this evening elementary school work is essential. The most important factor in reorganization is efficient leadership.

DATE DUE

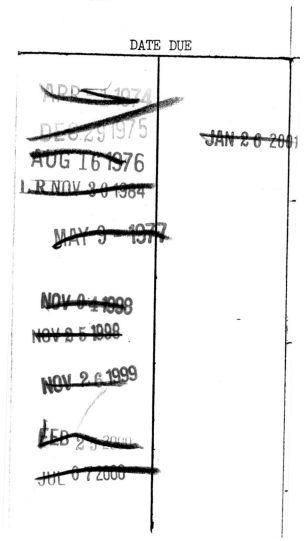

To Roger:

Hoping you enjoy
these attempts at
remembering simpler
but no less frustrating
times.

Dan Aaron

Being Born

and Other Simple Pleasures

by

Dan Graves

authorHOUSE™

1663 LIBERTY DRIVE, SUITE 200
BLOOMINGTON, INDIANA 47403
(800) 839-8640
WWW.AUTHORHOUSE.COM

First published by AuthorHouse 01/18/05

ISBN: 1-4208-1787-6 (sc)

Library of Congress Control Number: 2004099708

Printed in the United States of America
Bloomington, Indiana

This book is printed on acid-free paper.

ACKNOWLEDGEMENTS

Special thanks to Mari Emsweller for having the patience to edit a manuscript that looked like it had been through a bush hog demonstration.

Also, to her husband Jeff, who with his experience as a newspaper publisher, offered encouragement when he knew he should have been trying to talk me out of it. Special thanks to Don Polston and his computer while trying to make my artwork look halfway presentable. It's amazing how much patience some people have.

To all the chickens of the world. Without their help, the first part of this book would not have been possible.

TABLE OF CONTENTS

FORWARD

A writer, especially one who hopes to see his or her name on a book, lives with a dreadful fact. The competition is fierce. Every person who has done anything more exciting than throw up on the doctor at birth wants to write a book, either about their life or someone else's, a fictional novel on submarine warfare, or the steamy, but troubled passion between lovers on an English estate during the Victorian period. Bookstores overflow with publications on every conceivable, and in some cases, inconceivable subjects that range from how to construct a pocket sized nuclear weapon to the proper way to blow your nose in public.

Into this seething mass of a dog-eat-dog world, I am casting my lot, hoping to shoulder out at least a small portion of space to plant my flag and take my place among the thousands of others who know the value of being able to ask at a cocktail party, "Have you read my book?" You are suddenly elevated to a lofty position, the center of attention, and showered with admiration and envy. At least, that's what I've been told. My years as a columnist has elicited a different response from my readers, the most common being, "where do you come up with all that b—-s—-?"

Another reality is one faced by all writers, no matter how acclaimed or notorious they happen to be. Their work may well realize some moderate success, most likely being sold in the area where the author is best known, or from family and friends who coerce others into buying the thing. Inevitably, the day arrives when, rummaging around in an antique or second hand store, the author finds his book stuffed in among hundreds of others with a little sticker on it showing a price of twenty-five cents. Here is his masterpiece, created through seemingly endless hours of emotional stress and sacrifice, the embodiment of pride and accomplishment, looking ragtag and worn, selling for a measly quarter. My only hope is that this publication will start at a cheap price and save me the shame of seeing it suffer a radical depreciation rate. This isn't a used car, you know.

Some books start with a preface, which according to Webster is a preliminary statement by the author or editor of a book, setting forth its purpose or expressing acknowledgement of assistance. This book really has no purpose other than to inflate the ego of its author. As for acknowledging assistance, all the credit must go to my wife Judy. With her encouraging expressions of faith in my ability she helped me through those depressing times of discouragement and brain death. She also has a nightstick, the type used by policemen who patrol the streets in big cities. When I had the urge to indulge in other pastimes, the whap, whap of the stick across her palm kept me motivated.

An introduction, such as this, is a so-called brief outline of the history of the book and the motivation of the author to write it, or an excuse for the book itself. Since it is based on my columns in various publications and spiced with a distorted imagination, it cannot be explained or excused. Its motivation has been adequately explained.

In order to keep the readers interest, the author of this book has decided to follow the guidelines of today's preferred literary subject material. It contains outright lies, juicy confessions, and the occasional fiction masquerading as a true story.

What the heck, give it a try. It might be a refreshing change of pace from the biographies and stories about tinseltown celebrities, football flummery, and overpaid, oversexed, but always innocent, Washington dignitaries. At least the reader may learn to appreciate the end result of an effort being driven by the threatening whap, whap of a night stick across a palm.

On the other hand, you say, who would be interested in reading the ramblings of a total stranger, even in a book as small as this? To answer that, I can only ask if you knew Samuel Clemens or Ernest Hemingway personally. Does Tom Clancy live next door? Does the author have to be a rock n' roll icon, a famous movie star, or a past president to capture a reading audience? If it helps, I once played a role in a local theatrical production of Arsenic And Old Lace, and the locals tried to get me to run for mayor in the year 2000. So there!

Read on to see what an almost famous person has to say.

LIFE ON THE FARM

*(Just because I don't eat cracked corn or scratch in the dirt
doesn't mean I don't lay an occasional egg.)*

Ask anyone who spent their pre-teen years in the
country what they thought of it and you'll get a variety of
answers. For most, country life was a mixture of blessings
and tribulations. Rural life for a kid offered a playground of
almost unlimited size with few of the restrictions suffered by
city slickers, such as avoiding strangers and not playing in
the streets. No one was a stranger and one car a day passing
the house was considered a traffic jam. A country kid learns
to appreciate a mostly quiet solitude and the freedom of
whizzing in the bushes without worrying about an audience.
On the other hand, a city kid never has to worry about being
a nursemaid to a bunch of finicky chickens.

Ours was a small spread with a barn and numerous
outbuildings, including a chicken coop and an "external
plumbing facility", or outhouse to the uneducated. Water
was pumped from a well, and although the first few gushes
had the color of weak blood from the rusty iron pipes and
tasted like the slurry from a steel mill, us kids were told it

1

was a good source of the iron we needed to remain healthy. I failed to see the benefits and refused to drink it unless it was flavored with Kool-Aid.

Unfortunately, our playground happened to be occupied by a bunch of scruffy critters that needed what seemed like constant feeding and care, and it was our station in life to see to it that they received it.

In our family, age determined your station in life and each of us were assigned daily tasks according to what we could handle physically. We didn't have a farm in the true sense of the word: only a few paltry acres where we kept a cow, or sometimes two, yearly litters of pigs, and a flock of chickens that furnished eggs and Sunday dinners. My sister, being the youngest and of course, a girl, was responsible for household chores, while my brother, being the oldest, threw hay to the cows and slopped the hogs. I was assigned to keeping the chickens from feeling unloved and chasing our resident duck out of the garden.

By the time I was old enough to associate "chicken" with various breeds of flightless, egg laying fowl with the IQ of a bowling ball, I had developed a grudging dislike for these critters, mainly because I was forced to see to their comfort. Every morning I carried a bucket of feed to their coop where I would be surrounded by a flock of squawking, flapping old hens scrabbling to get a place at the feed trough. The scene resembled the doors opening on a closeout sale at Big Lots.

Having drawn them off the nest, I gathered eggs while slithering around in droppings mixed with feathers and straw. To add insult to injury, Mom decided to include a flock of Banty hens and a foul tempered rooster to the herd, probably to add a little variety and color to the otherwise drab, retarded residents of Chicken City. Because of their

2

diminutive size, they or their eggs were never eaten and they were allowed to have the run of the place.

A mutual dislike immediately developed between myself and the Banty rooster, a colorful and cocky little fellow with the attitude of a grizzled old honeydipper. He apparently considered the farm as his territory and me as an interloper, which resulted in my being the target of frequent attacks at feeding time. He would appear from nowhere and commence flogging and pecking around my legs like a feathered, midget terrorist. Kicking and yelling as he beat around my feet, I'd retreat to the house with him at my heels where I would swear to retrieve Dad's shotgun and end his miserable life. I would stand inside the screen door and watch as he strutted around the back yard, clucking and squawking, looking like David after a run-in with Goliath. I hated that chicken.

Unlike the larger spreads surrounding our little haven, our herds of critters were small enough for each citizen to have a name, with the exception of most of the chickens. Even a few of those scroungy laggards had a handle. I understood the purpose of naming our dogs since every mutt in the area came from the same family tree, and ours and all their relatives showed up at the back door at suppertime. Only the ones we knew by name were fed.

But, some of the cows, hogs, ducks, and privileged chickens that roamed the place seemed to me better left unidentified. After all, it was difficult to invite something to dinner, especially as the main course, after you had been on a first name basis with it only that morning. For that reason a number of unnamed volunteers were kept in the chicken coop for weekend dinners.

On rare occasions, an adventuresome yard bird would wander onto the road and disappear in a cloud of feathers on the bumper of a passing pick-up truck. If it had a name we would grieve for the loss of a family member and have chicken and dumplings on a weekday. Since a select few of the poultry on Chaos Acres roamed free, I took a somewhat lighter view of such incidents since it meant fewer beaks to feed.

Dinnertime always took on the semblance of a grand Broadway production with a cast of thousands. Mom had a magnificent soprano voice that she used in the church choir, a couple of radio programs she hosted, and for calling hogs and kids. Most times we were a quarter-mile away at mealtime and her call to vittles wouldn't be heard, but rather felt as a vibration in the atmosphere, somewhat like the shock waves from a distant explosion. We weren't the only ones to respond to her siren-like wail, as every living thing that could detect her high notes sat up and took notice.

Arriving home, we waded through a crowd of critters on the porch who had also responded to her call to chow. Mom's pet sow Oontsie, a duck, chickens, and enough mixed breed dogs to pull a hay wagon, milled around like a bunch of Bowery bums waiting for the doors to open on a soup kitchen. Whatever showed up would either be shooed away or made to come in and wash behind its ears.

Evening meals were the main event, while breakfast, being less publicized, were normally quiet as the family sat in a groggy stupor and consumed anything set before it. That is, almost anything. Like all normal kids, there were certain concoctions we considered poisonous, their only purpose being to reduce the world over-population by killing some of us. On that list were oatmeal, grits, any green vegetable, liver, dumplings, corn that wasn't still on the cob, and anything Mom called her "special". These specials normally consisted of whatever happened to be left over from the previous week stirred into an unrecognizable goo and baked under a layer of cornbread mix. On those occasions, we wondered if we were products of planned parenthood or simply mistakes to be eliminated.

At the age of sixteen my brother's attention shifted from cows and hogs to cars and women. Now a man of the world, he needed wheels of his own. Weeks of badgering resulted in Dad parting with $75 for a 1927 Model A Ford that to my brother Ray was no better than a honey wagon. To me it represented everything I had dreamed about in personal transportation. Its graceful swooping fenders flowing smoothly over wire wheels blended harmoniously with the flat windshield and large rectangular grill. Bolted to the squared-off back end was a very continental looking spare tire. The hood had been removed to reveal the mighty four cylinder engine, and overall, it was light years ahead of any form of transportation that required kid power to motivate it, such as my bicycle.

At first my brother accepted it grudgingly, considering it an embarrassment. But when he discovered that girls loved to ride in it, his attitude toward Myrtle, as Mom named it, changed. For a while he was satisfied with his image as the guy who drove the old "T". Within a year the novelty had worn off and he managed to move up to a newer car, one that was only fifteen years old, and I inherited Myrtle. Even during those pre-historic times the legal driving age was sixteen, and since I was only twelve, I was prohibited from venturing onto the road. After a week of traumatizing the yard birds by chasing them around the apple orchard, Mom used Myrtle to clear a makeshift road in the woods next to the house and warned me of the consequences of finding a flat chicken in the orchard.

A normal Saturday at our place took on the appearance of winter quarters for The Ringling Bros., Barnum and Bailey Circus. Every kid within a two-mile radius, accompanied by their dogs, would gather for rides in the "T". The usual load was no less than six kids and an equal number of dogs. To visualize the scene, keep in mind that these dogs weren't "city slickers". Their main purpose in life was lazing around barn yards, scratching fleas, and serving as warning devices for stray skunks, foxes, and neighborly visitors. Their ancestry could be traced back to the same father, and since they were probably born of a brother/sister mating, they had about as much class as a rusty gate hinge. Also, they were neither fond of riding in automobiles or each other. A typical ride consisted of a dog either slobbering down the back of your neck, scrabbling frantically to get out of the car, or jerking hair out of the neck of another dog. Coupled with a hoard of kids trying to get clear of the mayhem and the scene resembled a firecracker at a mule auction.

The rule was: if you brought a dog it had to go along on the ride. Because of their well deserved reputation as chicken lovers, Mom didn't have time to keep her eye on a herd of four-legged rabble in the absence of their owners. Emptying the car looked remarkably like the entire seventh grade class arriving at a dog show with their low class entrants.

Then one day, Mom decided I needed some experience driving on a real road in real traffic, although the chances of meeting another vehicle on our lane was slim to none. With her riding shotgun and barking orders like a drill sergeant, we lurched off. Topping a small hill we gained speed as our pre-planned turn-around point approached. A healthy push on the mechanical brakes at the foot of the hill produced nothing but white knuckles and dilated pupils.

I took the only course of action I considered available and looked for solid objects to serve as a brake. They narrowed down to a sturdy looking telephone pole, so I steered straight into it. Later, Mom compared the sound at impact to someone swatting a giant dinner bell as our noses stopped inches short of the windshield. Those old cars, unlike today's tin boxes, were built tough, many of which could have mounted guns and served in modern tank warfare.

With no damage to anything, not even the bumper, my on-road driving career ended and I returned to the trail in the woods.

By summer's end, Myrtle, with a broken transmission, was sold and I returned to the bicycle for mechanized transportation. The old girl had developed a real personality and her demise was a painful one for me. As she was towed away I felt the same sorrow one would feel while watching their frail, pleading grandmother being drug away in chains. Since then I've often thought that if Mom had changed her meal call an octave or two, Myrtle would have eventually showed up at the back door, broken transmission and all, along with the rest of the crowd.

Since a persons standing in the kid social pecking order is measured by his or her possessions, my popularity level bottomed out and the local dogs stopped shying away from our place on Saturday. Once again I had to take my place in the order of common peons, to be remembered as the kid who used to own the "T".

PENAL INSTITUTIONS, COW PIES, AND LUCKY STRIKES

(If you ain't tried it before, you'd best talk to someone who has. On the other hand, you cain't hardly trust a moonshiner to tell the truth.)

The end of summer brought with it shorter days, colorful trees, and that most dreaded of times, the return to school. We were forced to go shopping for new clothes, even though as far as we were concerned, the rags we wore through the summer with their grass stains and smears of not quite dry meadow muffins were quite acceptable. Books were purchased along with a new pair of tennis shoes for gym class. Those things defied any excuse for their creation. Being nothing more than molded slabs of rubber bonded to god-awful looking pieces of black canvas that laced up to the ankle, they represented the bottom of the heap in the fashion world. Wearing those ill-fitting monstrosities, we would pad onto a basketball court with feet making obnoxious slapping sounds and looking like we had just returned from wading in a tar pit. Because of those shoes and shorts that

8

made me look like a stork wearing a parachute, I've always considered sports requiring such garb as havens for the fashionably challenged.

The first two months of imprisonment dragged by in what seemed years as we anxiously awaited the anticipated next phase of seasonal fun. Winter was approaching and with it came the longed for ingredient. Finally, the weatherman would make the glorious announcement. A big snow would be forecast, hopefully a ten-incher, and also hopefully, on a school day. Unlike today when even the threat of snow will shut down the entire state, it took at least ten inches of the stuff to close our local penal institutions.

After a summer of storage, our sleds had a healthy layer of rust on the runners. For some reason, we always forgot this fact and the first sledding snow saw us standing at the crest of Dead Man's Hill, ready for the plunge into the briar patch below. We were confident that with our skill at maneuvering, we could avoid the pitfalls of hidden rocks and sticky bushes while savoring the rush of wind past our ears and the thrill of speed.

Standard protocol called for a running start and a belly flop onto the sled just over the crest of the hill. For some reason, rust against snow has about the same frictional resistance as ankle tight pegged pants over size twelve tennis shoes. The next ten minutes would be spent digging snow out of various bodily orifices after the rider had slid twenty feet on his nose when the sled stopped like it had been tied to a fence post. Then, the runners were cleaned and contests held to see who could go the furthest on a freshly opened trail. Once a trail was made, everyone stuck with it except those adventuresome types who volunteered to blaze new ones. Selecting a new path, the trailblazer would launch into the unknown. If he survived, the rest would follow.

Normally, cattle would be pastured on the hill, adding a new dimension to the excitement. Only rusty runners could stop a sled faster than an old meadow muffin hidden beneath the snow. Streaking downhill with our eyes streaming from the cold and wind, an occasional rider would suddenly find himself all alone, skimming six inches above the snow, his sled having stopped abruptly against a frozen pile of bovine excrement. Just before nose contact, your mind would recoil at the possibility of plowing into another deposit, this one from a cow with diarrhea. Small rocks and briars could be removed and the wounds healed by a kiss from Mom, but she drew the line when it came to sympathizing with a dung covered kid.

Frozen ponds became ideal spots for improvised hockey games using sticks and rocks for pucks. These routs took on the appearance of group floggings as sticks swung wildly, resulting in numerous "goose egg" lumps and skinned legs. The only thing safe from harm was the puck because no one ever hit it.

Unlike city slickers, we didn't have the luxury of a nearby five and dime, nor the money to spend on man-made entertainment. We lived by a simple philosophy: if it didn't bite, sting, or spray you with a noxious fluid, it could more than likely be used for some form of fun.

By the end of February cabin fever was taking its toll. It was too cold and snow had lost its magic, now being no more than a hindrance that made feeding the chickens and gathering eggs an even more hated chore. Tempers were short and school was a prison filled with evil wardens and low-life inmates. One winter, while looking for diversions until spring brought the world back to life, we resorted to measures more desperate than pelting each other with dried cow chips and rotten eggs. It was time to venture into that realm of forbidden fruit, the epitome of courage that would elevate us to hairy-chested he-men at the risk of severe retaliation from our parents.

Smoking!

For years we had watched our fathers fire up and apparently enjoy Lucky Strikes, Camels, and Prince Albert pipe tobacco. Frequently, Dad would go on an austerity campaign and roll his own. Curling a paper between two fingers of one hand, he used the other to shake tobacco from a draw string pouch. Spreading the weed evenly along the length of the paper, he rolled it into a cylinder, licked one edge to seal it, and twisted the ends shut. Today, that misshapen torpedo would get him arrested on the spot.

Fascinated by the tendrils of smoke curling from nostrils and smoke rings being blown, we decided to experience for ourselves the enjoyment our fathers apparently got from the sport. Of course, the first step was to decide where to start. Operating on limited finances, we decided to start with a cigar, primarily because a cigar would be less costly than a pack of cigarettes and could be stretched a long way due to its size.

A plan was devised. One of us would be chosen as the purchasing agent and the other two would serve as advisors. I drew the short straw. Riding the two miles into town on our bicycles, I entered the drug store as the advisors stood on the sidewalk and watched through the window. I looked over the selection in a glass case and decided on a 5-cent Home Made that looked pretty classy with a bright yellow band and wrapped in shiny cellophane.

The clerk eyed me suspiciously.

"I'll take one of those" I said, pointing at the yellow box.

"What do you plan to do with it?" he asked.

"It's for my dad."

"I thought your dad was a cigarette smoker."

Dang! How was I to know this guy knew my Dad? "He's, uh———switching," I said as small beads of sweat formed on my forehead.

"If I sell you that cigar the only switching at your house will be the one applied to your rear end."

Apparently, if we were going to experience the pleasure of being men of the world we would have to improvise. The only alternatives that came to mind were a soda straw, ironweed stalks, or hay chaff from the barn loft.

By comparison to other smoking materials with regards to mellowness and flavor, a soda straw doesn't make it to the first rung of the ladder. A lot depends on whether it's a paper or plastic straw. We tried the paper type. When lit, it alternately spit flames and sputtered while emitting little puffs of foul smelling smoke. Admittedly, it draws freely, but leaves an aftertaste on the tongue similar to what one could expect from gnawing on a ten-year-old tennis shoe.

Discarding the straw idea, we harvested a few ironweeds from the previous years crop that stood in the pasture, their stems vaguely resembling a dirty brown cigarette. Unfortunately, they also harbored various insects that revived in the warmth when the end was lit. Not only did the smoke taste as bad as the straw, it was filled with numerous small critters that did nothing to enhance the flavor. So far, the possibility of our becoming suave, debonair men of the world was skating on thin ice.

Spitting and coughing, we filched an old corncob pipe from Dad's collection and loaded it with hay chaff. We didn't know it at the time, but any chaff smoker will tell you that the best quality comes from either timothy or clover fields. Our hayloft contained a few remnants of what was apparently gunpowder-dry skunk weed from the previous year's crop, which we packed into the pipe and set afire. Like a small Roman candle it spit sparks and an occasional gout of flame. Passing it from hand to hand, each of us took a long drag and sucked it down.

Simultaneously, sounding like the cheerleading squad from Sunnyside Sanitarium, we exploded in ragged coughing and hacking. Being trapped in a burning outhouse would have been a kinder fate than taking another puff off that devils weed. By now we were feeling a little queasy but no less determined to experience the pleasures our dads, no doubt, got from smoking.

There was only one course of action left. The real thing! The ash trays in our house always held a supply of butts, and after a bit of stealthy maneuvering around Mom, we slithered back to the barn with a handful of Lucky Strike remnants. Firing up, we sucked until our cheeks collapsed and inhaled.

WHAM! The world reeled before our eyes. Couldn't breathe! Stomachs churned! Gagging and retching we stumbled from the barn, convinced that Sir Walter Raleigh had been the world's dumbest whacko. Adolph Hitler and Rasputin had nothing on that guy. Even the thick, gray, evil tasting goop called Dr. Drakes Elixir which our mothers forced down us by holding our noses until our mouth popped open, and touted to cure everything from warts to ingrown toenails, tasted like Kool-Aid by comparison.

With the world swimming before our eyes and staggering like drunks, we swore off smoking forever. Never would we cross swords with our fathers. Anyone who could handle that stuff was not to be messed with.

The next few months passed slowly as the dreary browns and grays of the countryside began turning green with the return of leaves and the hated grass on our lawn. Life returned to the barnyard as the chickens, determined to raise a brood, refused to allow the eggs to be gathered. Hogs rooted around in fresh spring mud. Bicycles were rescued from winter storage and a renewed vigor was experienced by all. Dad, recalling his childhood and improvised playthings, made each of us a pair of stilts from small sassafras trees on which we stumped around like Frankenstein monsters. Uncharacteristically, he then announced he would make a pair of the world's tallest stilts and demonstrate them himself. Selecting a pair of tall sassafras saplings, he trimmed them and nailed on two wooden blocks eight feet from the ground. Leaning them against the house, he climbed a ladder and mounted up while Mom and I served as the ground crew, steadying them while he got his balance.

Pushing away from the house, Dad realized he should have delayed his feat for a year until the sassafras had had a chance to season. The poles began bowing out in an arch while Dad tried valiantly to hang on, his arms and legs forming a large X as the arch widened. For an instant, the scene took on the appearance of a form of medieval torture, while I expected the poles to suddenly straighten and launch him over the house. Finally reaching his limit of stretchability, he let go of one pole, wrapped his arms and legs around the other and began the long return to earth, looking like a sailor clinging to the mast of a sinking ship. The only result was a wounded pride and a bruised butt from the landing. I carved another notch on the pistol grip of grown-up responsibility, right next to the one for smoking.

As the days lengthened, flowers grew and the residents of Chaos Acres returned to their usual warm weather routines, like a Phoenix rising from the ashes of winter. The dogs abandoned their houses and spent hours stretched in the sun, scratching and yawning like Bowery bums. Even the dreaded chickens left the coop and began foraging on their own, although I was still required to supplement their diet on a daily basis. Bees flitted among the blossoms in the apple orchard, mushrooms popped up in the woods, and birds sang in the trees. Valhalla had returned. Except for one thing. Grass.

All winter I had prayed that the bitter cold would kill the accursed stuff once and for all, but to no avail. It began growing in profusion, especially around the spots where the dogs had laid their logs. It was my responsibility to keep it in check.

Powered mowers were rare, and with over an acre of lawn it was a daunting task for a push mower manned by a reluctant kid. Despite my grousing and whining, I was informed that future meals depended on keeping the lawn from becoming a home for any of the local wildlife. Now, not only was I responsible for keeping our scruffy chickens happy, I had to make it easier for them to strut and scratch and occasionally flog me through the back door. With my prayers for winter induced kill unanswered, I began hoping that one of the B-36 bombers that frequently flew high overhead would lose a bomb and wipe out not only the lawn, but the chicken coop as well. When it didn't happen, I tackled another season of grass that grew faster than I could control it.

In spite of such drawbacks, it was now time for my brother and I to add to our already burgeoning menagerie while also ruffling Mom's feathers. We could start scouring the woods to see what had fallen out of a nest or wandered away from its den.

WATCH WHO YOU CALL
AN ANIMAL

The word "animal" and the definition of it is a travesty to the true nature of what we qualify as the lesser inhabitants of this planet. In fact, my relationship with so-called animals (with the exception of chickens) proved far more pleasant than my contacts with those of my own kind. I never had an animal cheat me out of my favorite shooter marble, nor did an animal turn me into the parent police for some simple infraction of the rules.

Dogs figured more prominently than any other species of four-legged family members. Most of our mutts had about as much class as a hay baler, being of "mixed breeds", which was a way of saying, third generation removed of a combination of coyote and junk yard guardian. When asked by anyone what lineage our pets claimed, we referred to them as "part used auto parts emporium patrol specialist and part poultry acquisition agent."

"What's its name?" was always the second question.

"Depends on the occasion. In good times we call him Specs De La Montmorency Jones, or Specs for short. If he's caught in the chicken coop, Dad calls him Goner."

From a monetary standpoint, they wouldn't have brought more than two dollars on the open market. However good a hundred dollar dog would have been for sitting in laps, one couldn't be used to chase hogs out of the garden. Ours excelled at that and sleeping, snapping at flies, and showing up for dinner within ten seconds of the same time every day. As for their loyalty to us, it was unwavering, being based on an agreement that as long as they were fed they would grace us with their presence.

Numerous attempts were made to train them to roll over, sit up, or shake a paw. Teaching one of them anything was no more successful than briefing a three-year-old on Einstein's Unified Field Theory Of Relativity. All such efforts resulted in nothing more than the student lying on its back with four feet in the air and its tail curled between its legs, tapping a rhythm on its stomach. In spite of these shortcomings they did the job they were hired to do. The property was kept free of stray cats that hoped to use our barn as a maternity ward and other curs that liked to snatch a chicken now and then. We were greeted at the school bus every day, much to the annoyance of the driver who had to wait while we yelled and whistled them from under and in front of the bus. They tolerated our jokes and sometimes dirty tricks, such as pieces of bread spread with liberal amounts of peanut butter. Or, in the case of my little sister, being dressed in the latest doll fashions.

The only strain in relations came when the female hung out the sign that said she was receiving male suitors. In spite of our precautions, we had our share of small, fuzzy, very mixed breed lumps that were abandoned by the hussy within two weeks, leaving Mom with the task of seeing to it that they were raised as responsible citizens. Once they were weaned, we kids spent days roaming the countryside, armed with a pup and knocking on doors. Sometimes successful, the common reactions were, "no thanks", "beat it kid", or "I haven't worn out the last one you gave us".

Why do we keep dogs? Perhaps the better question is, why do they put up with us? In the country, dogs were as natural as paint on a pump. Every farm had at least two hounds, none of which were any more useful than concrete lawn elves.

Although dogs were inevitable, living in the sticks had the advantage of offering a wide variety of potential pets, some of which came from the barn. Mom had a sow which she had bred yearly, and the resulting litter, when marketable, furnished her a meager sum she called her bread and butter money. One fall, the old girl (the sow, that is), miscalculated and had one more piglet than her supply of faucets. Unable to compete for room at the dinner table, it became stunted and sickly.

Mom adopted it, strictly from a financial standpoint, and brought it into the house where she hand fed it from a bottle. As with every other critter on the place, she gave it a handle, calling it Oontsie. With a warm crate in the utility room and being hand fed, Oontsie recovered quickly and grew so rapidly that by spring she was not only housebroken, but weighed about as much as a pot bellied stove.

While Oontsie considered herself a member of the household, Mom thought otherwise. For a while, the porker was allowed free reign of the property, finally being penned in the barn only at night. She spent the days roaming the back yard and making a nuisance of herself with us while keeping the dogs in a constant uproar. Any attempts by us at outdoor games that included running or wrestling on the ground resulted in a 200 pound hog joining in. Being rooted around became commonplace.

We soon learned that once a hog has experienced the comforts of home, there is no way to convince it to settle for living in a barn. Having spent the winter in the house luxuriating beside the stove convinced Oontsie that that was her rightful place. On numerous occasions she would shove past us and rumble into the house like a small elephant, only to be met by Mom and her broom. One of us would hold open the screen door and Mom would whack the squealing hog outside. Oontsie sealed her fate as smoky links and sausage patties the day she bowled me over and entered *through* the screen door. After the dust cleared from a shattered screen door frame, torn screen wire and an atmosphere full of broom bristles, we knew she would soon be "bread and butter" money.

A local barn supplied the next wedge between normal parent/child relations. Homer the pigeon, who was kidnapped from the nest and raised from a fledgling, quickly established himself as a capital pest. Orders were given to give him back to his natural element, but he refused to leave, sitting in a pear tree by the back door during the day and roosting in our barn at night. Within seconds of leaving the back door you had a pigeon sitting on your head. Although we kids didn't mind this, Mom had reservations about hanging out laundry with a bird roosting in her hair. His eviction notice came when, riding south end first on my brother's head, he left a stream of excrement dripping from his nose. Homer was driven fifteen miles to an abandoned quarry and turned loose where he joined a flock of his brethren, never to "darken" our heads again.

The owl, captured by my brother, joined our clan reluctantly and because of a serious attitude problem, stayed only a short time. Placed in a washtub with a screen covering, it let us know immediately what it thought of our hospitality. Ray lifted the screen, stuck his hand into the tub and lost a small part off the end of one finger. He then gave the bird to me. My first act as the new beast master was to lift off the screen, kick the tub, and watch as the feathered chain saw flogged off into the woods. I was a strong believer in first impressions being a sign of things to come.

The squirrels were captured at an early age and soon became the darlings of the household. Even Mom couldn't fault the little fuzzballs as they scampered around on our shoulders and played like a couple of kittens. On the other hand, the dogs were in a state of constant confusion.

They were used to treeing the things, not seeing one sitting on someone's head. The little rodents were inseparable and when one of them fell into a large water bowl and drowned, the other was turned loose in the woods next to the house. For weeks we left a daily supply of food under a large beech tree and occasionally took the now fully grown squirrel for a ride on our shoulders. It was inevitable that he would eventually revert to the wild and when he finally disappeared, Mom firmly requested that we stick to socially acceptable pets. That meant that if it didn't bark, meow, moo, quack, or cluck it was persona non grata and could make its own way in the world without our help.

Fortunately, Parker, our nearest neighbor, had a zoo that he was willing to share with us, including a retarded old German shepherd named Bonehead, a pot-bellied burro, and a billy goat affectionately called John Henry. I took a liking to John Henry because of his lack of awareness that he was capable of anything more than eating and breathing. His days were spent standing like a stone in a small pasture, never moving except to go to the barn in the evening at feeding time.

One day, Parker, taking a break from stretching an electric fence around a small pasture, showed me that goats have a sense of humor. Walking up to John Henry he raised his boot and kicked the goat squarely between the huge pair of curled horns that adorned its head. Boy, that looks like fun, I thought. Slowly, ol' J.H. began backing up while shaking his head from side to side until ten yards separated them. Rearing on his hind legs, he cocked his head to one side and charged while Parker braced himself for the collision. I watched in awe as man and goat struggled against one another until Parker finally released his hold on J.H's horns and the goat returned to his usual comatose state. Apparently, John Henry's choice of entertainment was the reason for his obvious lack of any brain wave activity.

What happened next demonstrates the narrow gap of intelligence that exists between homo sapien young and the so-called lesser species. Obviously, Parker knew what made the goat happy, and since I was feeling a little bored myself, I walked up to John Henry, lifted my foot and belted him smartly between the eyes. Glaring at me through beady yellow and black eyes, he began his routine of head shaking and backing up. I braced myself for the charge, wondering if I had made a mistake and weighing the possibility of outrunning him. Too far to the fence, I thought as he launched himself at me like a hairy cannonball. Since I was lighter than Parker by a hundred pounds, the goat rammed me in the stomach and tossed me onto his back like a sack of wet grass. Hanging onto his horns, I slid down his nose and ended up with my rear sliding in the weeds, nose to nose, eyeball to eyeball with what looked like, at that distance, something from a nightmare. Afraid to let go for fear of being trampled, J.H., with me aboard, didn't slow down for the new electric fence, resulting in thirty yards of wire and posts being uprooted as Parker ran along behind, yelling and swatting at the goat.

Over an embankment and down into a gully, the show ended with me being wallowed in a rock filled dry stream bed like a feed bag in a pen full of Blue Tic pups. Parker finally convinced John Henry that the fun was over and I spent the rest of the day replacing fence posts and re-stringing wire while plotting ways to get even with that goat. The matter was taken out of my hands when a few weeks later, lightning struck a tree, under which both John Henry and Bonehead were taking refuge from a storm. My last earthly sight of these two characters were bloated bodies, their legs stiff and pointing straight up like a scene from an Alfred Hitchcock movie. It gave me no pleasure.

We turned professional when one day my brother sneaked quietly into our bedroom and introduced me to Teddy, a fully grown red fox he had acquired in a trade. Supposedly housebroken and docile, Teddy proved to be a novel addition to the family. Being a nocturnal creature, he spent his days asleep in a dark corner of a bedroom and nights padding nervously through the house. By this time, the dogs, having experienced the squirrels and resigned to living with a crazy family, paid little attention, other than keeping a wary eye on Teddy when he was leashed and put outdoors.

Preparation of meals would sometimes bring the fox to the kitchen where he would sit like a pup until Mom threw him a hambone or other scraps. These he would take to the library room, scrape up a fold in a rug, lay the prize into it and tamp it over with his nose. A couple of times a week Mom would shake the rugs, collect the booty and throw it away, no doubt leaving the fox in a constant state of frustration.

The novelty of having a fox as a house pet, especially the reaction when he trotted in to greet guests who were unaware of him, wore off when he stole a pair of Mom's favorite house slippers, tore them to shreds and capped it off by piddling in the middle of her bed. Under pressure from the Commander-In–Chief, my brother made another transaction involving a rusty old gun and Teddy moved on to another unsuspecting household. Somehow, it didn't seem fitting to exchange a novel house pet for something as useless as a broken broom handle, but when given the option of getting rid of the fox or buying a pair of house slippers and washing bedclothes on those occasions when Teddy got careless, we opted for the easy way out.

(Nowadays, if a kid gets caught cussing, he's sent to his room with a stern warning. Back then, he arrived in his room accompanied by the fine taste of Ivory soap in his mouth.)

During the so-called formative years, we kids considered the task of educating adults as both difficult and sometimes hazardous. We prepared for the coming years of parental manipulation with intense concentration on innocent looks, various methods of denial, dumb stares, and a broad range of reasons why we shouldn't be held responsible for any event that wasn't witnessed first hand. In other words, if you didn't get caught, you didn't do it. In spite of all our preparation, our parents would get unruly on occasions and downright surly when something didn't suit them.

At times we wondered if our training of adults was paying off, especially in the area of the fine arts. Our town was the heart of the limestone industry and we were fortunate to have one of the largest and best known carving mills within a half-mile of Chaos Acres. Highly skilled stone carvers, known throughout the world for their creations of decorative architecture and life-like statues, practiced their trade at this site.

Part of the process included the making of full size plaster casts of each design to be used as models for the actual carving. Upon completion of the project, these casts were discarded in a heap behind the buildings.

One day a friend and I discovered this treasure trove and began carting them home where we decorated the back yard with a variety of lion heads, elaborate floral and scroll works, and partial busts of Greek gods and (in)famous past political figures. For a short while our place took on the appearance of the epicenter of the fall of the Roman Empire.

My parents viewed these treasures in a different light however, and ordered us to return them to the junk heap. According to Dad, eating plaster could make the hogs sick. A flimsy excuse as far as I was concerned, but back to the scrap heap went Generals Lee and Grant, Zeus, Thor, and a number of angels and evil looking gargoyles. Here was history being flushed down the stool like so much cheap toilet paper.

In spite of being disappointed at their lack of cultural appreciation, I believe my parents were subliminally affected by the incident. Mom began dabbling in oil painting, discovering a talent she uses to this day. Dad became quite proficient at the building trades as he tore the house down around us and "remodeled" it. Unfortunately, he did so with every home we lived in after that. I now hate the smell of wall board and saw dust.

Training older people, such as grandparents, proved to be a much more difficult and daunting task. For years we had a variety of house guests in the form of relatives whom Mom had taken in. My great-grandfather spent his final years with us, sitting in his rocker, smoking cigars that smelled like smoldering linoleum, and wielding his cane with surprising accuracy to the stomach of supposed antagonists. Gentle by nature, he left himself wide open for the imagination of kids and the occasional practical joke.

Exploding matches were my favorite. The first time I offered him a light his surprise was genuine. At the loud pop he lurched back in his rocker and instinctively reached for his cane. After that, his feigned surprise had me wondering if I would ever be able to break him of the habit of falling for that one.

With no malice intended, another incident caused me to write him off as hopeless, a lost babe in the jungle of nasty little two-legged rug rats like myself. I offered him a piece of candy I had fashioned from a well used and grimy ball of wallpaper cleaner. Everyone else in the house had accepted my offering with the understanding I would get it back for inclusion in the next batch of "fudge". Grandpa hadn't read the rule book.

Popping the grungy wad into his mouth he chewed for a few seconds while the look of a man turning into a werewolf contorted his features. I stood in awe as his throat constricted and he swallowed the mess. Mom appeared, and by the look on our faces it was apparent what had happened. When informed he had swallowed wallpaper cleaner, his only comment was, "I thought it tasted kinda funny." At that, I was given instructions to keep him informed of any future activities that involved inedibles.

After Grandpa's passing we stayed on the farm until homes were found for the dogs, sold or gave away the remainder of the livestock and prepared to move into town. I looked forward to life in the fast lane, and although it wasn't a big town, city life offered freedom from chickens and screen door bashing hogs. Not until later did I realize how life in the sticks had instilled in me an appreciation for elbow room and a love for the wild side of nature and its inhabitants. Every creature has a place and a purpose, even though I still consider chickens to be the result of an evolutionary mistake. According to paleontologists, birds are direct descendents of dinosaurs that once roamed the planet. I'm convinced that Mom's Banty rooster had a few leftover genes from a T-Rex floating around in its bloodstream. Thank goodness the little bugger had lost its teeth.

HICK FROM THE STICKS
TO SLICK FROM THE
CITY

The new house wasn't large or fancy by any standard, but it had a much smaller yard and the only livestock present was the neighbor's cat, a mangy sneaky-looking scoundrel with the disposition of an alcoholic hangman. Perched on a high bluff overlooking the river, our abode sat in a large square of grass, which meant less maintenance requirements and more time to expand the horizons of a new way of life. With three box-like bedrooms, living room, a kitchen and a half-basement, it came with a rickety dock on the river and two flat-bottomed river boats that bore a vague resemblance to the barges the ply the Ohio river; the kind used to haul coal. Constructed of wooden planking, they were equipped with oar locks and were ugly and heavy. In spite of their lack of sex appeal, Dad considered them as valuable accessories and was soon happily paddling around stretching trotlines along the river. I, on the other hand, being conscious of my social standing, viewed them from a different perspective.

The river was a popular spot for boaters from the Boating Club located a half-mile downstream, and on weekends an assortment of fancy runabouts pulling water skiers flashed by in front of our dock. As far as I was concerned, to be seen in one of Dad's scows by any member of the jet set would be the same as getting caught stealing chickens from an orphanage. Occasionally, Dad would request my help in running the trotlines, and it seemed, always on Sunday afternoon when traffic on the water was the heaviest. To save face, I couldn't slide down into the scow when another boat approached because of the slimy layer of water and dead night crawlers that perpetually sloshed around in it. So, I would assume a pose of total indifference and hope that no one I knew was in the passing craft. Finally, in a move to keep up with the Joneses, Dad purchased a sleek runabout, and later, a small skipjack racing boat. Now, with the playing field evened, the garbage scows became a source of amusement as my brother and I occasionally used them to "slum it" by using flat planks as paddles as we moved among the rest of the upper crust.

In spite of our new social standing, Dad set the ground rules for any thoughts we may have had about the use of the new boats. "If you take one of them out without adult supervision, you'd best take whatever worldly goods that mean anything to you along, because there will be no good reason to return." Faced with that threat, three friends and I decided one day to improvise a craft of our own design. Building materials were a wash tub unknowingly donated by someone's mother, a length of rope, and a truck tire inner tube inflated around the tub. Voila! Instant low cost boat.

Days of rain had left the river swollen and filled with all manner of floating junk. Undeterred, our plan was to attach the rope to a handle of the tub, launch the "boat" with a volunteer aboard and float downstream while a ground crew followed on the bank holding the rope in case it became necessary to rescue the craft and passenger. The others unanimously agreed that since it was my river, I should be the one to volunteer to explore the new frontier. Boarding was tricky, but I finally pushed away from the dock, sitting in the tub with arms and legs dangling in the water, looking like a spider in a thimble. The scene could best be described as:

Rub-A-Dub-Dub
One Retard In A Tub
And Three More Hoppin' On The Bank

I was amazed at the strength of the current and the amount of flotsam whizzing by the sleek craft. Realization that this thing could sink hit me but I wasn't about to request that the ground crew haul me in. After a hundred yards had passed without incident, I began to think I should travel this way more often. The discomfort of being scrunched in the tub was offset by the pleasure of feeling like I now ranked with such greats as Sir Edmund Hillary in exploring the unknown. Suddenly, I heard what sounded like a whoopee cushion deflating in a bowl of warm Jello. Something sharp had sneaked up from behind and holed the inner tube. The H.M.S. Laundry Room was going down.

Calmly, I informed the crew of my plight and requested to be pulled ashore. That was a mistake. "C'mon, you can make it. Paddle with your hands," they shouted. I informed them as diplomatically as possible, using only half my library of colorful metaphors, that the only way this thing was going, was down. I wasn't about to grab the rope and start hauling because they would simply let it go and I would have to explain to an angry mother that her wash tub would only be available again during the dry season.

With shouts of encouragement ringing in my ears I watched the inner tube fold over the rim of the tub and the rush of water as captain and vessel plunged toward the bottom. Only then did the scurvy shore crew pull in the tub, leaving me to find my own way ashore. I slogged through a layer of smelly debris and crawled out looking like I had been swimming in the slurry from a coal mine. Right then, I would have traded my so-called buddies for a coop full of hostile chickens. Even though I offered to repair the tube and let another delinquent try it, there were no takers. Maybe it was the look in my eye or the way I capped the offer with a prime expletive and a snicker when I said I would help man the rope.

As I vented my anger I became aware of the greater risk of using foul language. Grandma was still with us and I felt she could sense the vibrations in the atmosphere from a cuss word, even at this distance. At any moment she might appear and launch an attack with her bar of soap. With a final warning to my buddies not to reveal this failure to join the other great adventurers of our time to anyone, I slunk off to take a bath.

That summer saw the emergence of yet another complication in the lives of our gang of thugs. We were aware of the presence of girls in the world, but so far their reason for being was a total mystery. They were coddled. We were whipped. They dressed funny and we were taught to treat them with respect and to open doors and let them go ahead of us. If a dispute arose, they usually won and we were punished for our transgression. Contrary to the popular myth that pre-puberty males hate females, we simply gave them a wide berth and stuck our finger down our throat and made gagging noises when accused of showing interest in a particular girl. Suddenly, a higher, unseen power flipped the switch and girls were revealed from a different perspective. Accompanying this revelation were a number of physical disabilities, which included blushing, sweaty palms, and a shift in speech patterns that included stuttering and stammering. During the previous years, our dress codes had altered between railroad hobo and Salvation Army castoff. Only on Sunday morning when the families attended church were we transformed from Neanderthals to civilized homo sapiens, and then only under severe parental pressure. Now, faced with fluttering eyelashes, rosy lips, coy smiles and swiveling hips we began collapsing into creatures with two left feet and an unfamiliar desire for cleanliness, well groomed hair, and aftershave lotion, even though we weren't shaving. Although we managed to stumble around some handicaps, there was one that would prove insurmountable, at least for a while.

From our perspective, suave, debonair men needed suitable wheels if they were expected to impress the opposite sex. Our bicycles, which had been a source of pride prior to the advent of hormones, were now an embarrassment. Rather than be seen on a bicycle by that secret object of our affection, we began walking more and riding only when necessity dictated. Some members of our motley troupe had two, and others three years before they reached legal driving age, not to mention the fact that none of the girls would be allowed on an official date for the same period of time. Nonetheless, even old Myrtle, my former Model A would have elevated me to a higher plane, even if it did nothing but sit in the driveway. In the meantime, we were confined to lying about our conquests and, if the girl and her family were members of the same church, Sunday lunch accompanied by our parents. In three years I fell in and out of love so often that I had a difficult time remembering the name of the one to whom I had sworn my eternal affection the week before.

At the ripe age of fourteen I got caught in a love triangle of my own making. I had sealed my undying devotion to Anita by giving her an I.D. bracelet with our names engraved on it. We were going steady, whatever that meant. Then, at a church social, I met Karen, a cute brunette who happened to be the minister's daughter. Like a male lion I saw nothing wrong with collecting a harem, so I gave her an identical bracelet, also engraved with the same message. I was going steady – again. Like a bigamist supporting two households, neither of which was aware of the other, I flitted from flower to flower for a couple of months. My status with the guys soared and my ego grew like a baby elephant on steroids. However, Confucius say, "he who walk in swamp soon fall in quicksand". The plug was pulled from my horn of plenty one Sunday afternoon as I left a restaurant with Anita, just as Karen and her parents entered. I've never seen such a look of evil in the eyes of a sweet, young girl and I soon learned the truth in, Hell hath no fury like a woman scorned. Needless to say, one bracelet came back, while Anita, unaware of the deception, continued to wear hers in innocence. I wasn't about to confess my wrongdoing and lose the only remaining proof of my irresistible charm.

The tribulations of growing too fast, a deepening sense of independence, a total loss of reasoning power, and an ever increasing interest in the opposite sex created numerous upheavals in the family. Fighting to maintain control while struggling with resistance from siblings, especially boys, often causes parents to wonder about the wisdom of the old saying, "be fruitful and multiply". I know that at times my parents would have preferred that to mean, "operate an apple orchard and work part time as mathematicians".

SIXTEEN, CARS, AND PASSION PITS

My sixteenth birthday marked the turning point in my life from an ordinary, nameless face in the crowd to a suave, debonair, four-wheel knight in shining armor, ready for the local drag strip and wrestling matches at the passion pits. That was the year I became independently mobile, no longer requiring the services of a chauffeur. At the same time I lost my status as a common household nuisance and became downright dangerous to myself and an unsuspecting world. Immediately, I launched a campaign to acquire my own car by explaining to my parents that a Saturday night date in their four-door Chevy sedan would leave permanent scars on my social standing. The only thing left for me would be horned rim glasses, a pocket pencil protector, and white socks. Such slop didn't work, but when informed they would be spending every Saturday night at home for the next five years, Dad relented.

My first choice was a hot rod being offered for sale by a recent draftee into the Army. A '32 Ford roadster equipped with a V-8 big enough to furnish electricity for the entire state, it embodied every reason for my existence. So what if it didn't have a top? Umbrellas and tarps would suffice. Only a two-seater? No problem. I'd have just one friend at a time, and as for dating, I'd ask only one girl at a time and relieve the problem of overcrowding. Faced with such logic, Dad conceded defeat and arrangements were made to pick the thing up in a week. I could sense his skepticism about my driving what he referred to as "a grenade with the pin pulled", but I think he planned to borrow it himself for a few Saturday nights.

With only days left until the big event, friends brought me home from school. Sitting in the drive was a beautifully restored older Chevy convertible with glistening black paint, chromed wheels, and a white top to match the interior. We surrounded the car like buzzards on road kill while speculating on who its owner might be. In the house, Dad dropped the keys into my hand with a stern warning to treat it with respect and follow the rules. All thoughts of a hot rod vanished, which fit into my parents' plans quite well. Mom's plans, at least.

For six months I reveled in the notoriety of being associated with the car, until one day a screaming crash demolished the lovely machine and came close to snuffing out the lives of four teenagers. After a few months of recovery, I vowed never to drive again. Now, my parents were faced with the possibility of spending their Saturday nights cruising the strip and midnight drag races with me sitting in the back seat. Dad didn't mind the idea of racing some of the local hotfoots, but Mom would no doubt balk at flagging the contestants off the line. After all, if you weren't driving, protocol required that you contribute to the racing in some manner. And, how long could either of them put up with spending an evening in the concession stand of the drive-in theatre when I had a date? Clinging desperately to hope for their future, another car appeared in the driveway.

There followed a succession of paint jobs, bigger engines, floor shifts, dual exhausts, custom wheels, and proof of the saying, "paid on Friday, broke on Monday". At home, hex signs appeared over doorways while my parents spoke in whispers about an alien life form living in the house.

With bankruptcy looming while he tried to support my popularity, Dad finally informed me that the next automobile would be my responsibility to purchase and maintain. That started a lifelong love affair with used car lots. The scenario would generally go like this:

Driving by a used car lot I'd see the one automobile that would make it worthwhile to continue living. With its chrome and paint sparkling, for the bigger part, a sign in the window would read, "One Owner. Like New". As I walked around the object of my affection a salesman would emerge from a little shack no larger than a two-hole outhouse with rows of plastic flags fluttering from the eves.

"She's a beauty ain't she, son?"

"Uh, huh. How much you askin'?"

"Just got her in yesterday from a retired schoolteacher who decided to step down to something a little more fittin' to her image. Only got a hunnert thousand on her, the car I mean, new brakes and water pump (sometime during the Great Depression), new paint (covers the rust), a limited warranty of thirty minutes or until you get it off the lot, whichever comes first. Let me get the keys an' you can take her for a spin, the car I mean (there goes the warranty)."

He finally reveals the price, I stagger and clutch my chest, and he quickly throws in hubcaps and a spare tire. Jumper cables hooked to another car finally gets the thing going and it manages to make it back to the lot after a short drive. There, the new water pump whizzes all the coolant onto the blacktop. After assurances that such a minor inconvenience will be taken care of, he evaluates my old car and says that these models aren't in much demand these days. I would have expected that even if I had arrived in a 1936 Dual Cowl Phaeton, ala Duesenberg. Like a marriage, the deal is finalized after he agrees to right all the wrongs, and the Teachermobile will be ready the next day. A week later I was always sorry I hadn't insisted on a bumper hitch in the deal. I could have purchased a trailer and hauled a Clydesdale horse around to serve as a tow when the skunk of a car decided to stop moving on its own power. That idea was logical, but it would have been difficult to explain to a date and the people behind us in the drive-in why it was necessary to bring a plow horse to see Beach Blanket Bingo.

Years later, I still hadn't learned the lesson and after suffering through the budgetary constraints of marriage and a growing family, I went crazy again and purchased a sleek, rear-engined, open wheel race car. While waiting for the opportunity to earn a beginners license from a sanctioned racing organization, temptation got the best of me. Wheeling the little bullet from the garage, I planned to take a spin around the block, just to get a feel for the machine while trying to avoid the local police department. They seemed to take a dim view of race cars on their streets.

With my wife and son serving as the push team, numerous attempts were made to fire it up, but to no avail. Finally, my wife reluctantly agreed to follow instructions and ride in the cockpit while I pushed, hoping to get more speed. With gusto, I got the little bugger rolling at a fair clip and yelled for her to pop the clutch. It lurched and wadded me into the engine cowling just as the engine fired, sending four hundred decibals of ripping sound into my ears just inches away from the exhaust pipes, lunged forward and broke the middle finger on my right hand, which had caught in the pushbar. First crawling on my knees, then half running I yelled, "Clutch, Clutch." She stomped the clutch and brake simultaneously and again I slammed into the cowling as she revved the engine to keep it running. Skinned, deaf, and with a broken finger, I thought, Laurel and Hardy couldn't have done better in their finest hour.

Occasionally, as I look at my still disfigured finger, I feel small pangs of guilt for regressing to those glorious days of yesteryear when life was good and we would live forever as favored warriors in Valhalla. Life was simpler as well as more complex in some ways, but seemingly without the pressures brought on by adulthood. It's just as good today as it will be tomorrow and the day after, but I'm finding it easier to lean on those memories and take a few deep breaths while trying to keep in mind that:

There are goals and missions for which we strive

But we seem dissatisfied when we arrive.

Back then, life was an endless cauldron of new experiences and adventures with no end in sight of the succession of sunrise and sunset. There were no dissatisfactions because we had no goals. No matter how old you are, that is still partially true, and as far as I'm concerned, the party is continuing. Meanwhile, I plan to walk backwards once in a while and relive those times when the only thing wrong with the world was having to take a bath more than once a week. Most of us, when asked to relate something from our past that was a major influence in molding our character, can recall at least one thing that made an impression. Mine was that pillar of soul, the epicenter of the known civilized world, an oasis in the desert of rules and regulations, and the one place on earth where a person could go to establish relationships between the sexes. THE DRIVE-IN THEATRE.

In a small town the drive-in was the focal point of a person's social life where you could establish your standings by what you drove or who you were seen with. On Friday and Saturday night we could be found at the old passion pit sweating like steel workers trying to make intelligent small talk, especially if it was a first date. Trying to maintain simple subjects to avoid stuttering normally went like this:

Me: "Great, huh?"

Her: "What's great?"

Me: "The movie. I've heard it's a good one."

Her: "I wouldn't know. If you'd turn on the windshield wipers we might be able to see it."

Our cars were cared for like favored children, but the one thing that didn't seem important were windshield wipers. They served only to keep the wiper arm from scratching the windshield, so turning them on did nothing more than give the effect of looking through the bottom of a broken coke bottle. If it was necessary to start the engine to operate the wipers, thus saving battery power, we put our meager fuel supply in jeopardy. Normally, we ran on whatever fuel we could buy with loose change found under the rear seat. After all, we needed the money we made from part time jobs for supporting a life style in the fast lane. It never occurred to us that more than a couple of gallons of gasoline was a necessity if we were to remain mobile. Faced with the wiper crisis, it became necessary to ask her which she preferred; Coke and popcorn from the concession stand or a leisurely walk home after the car runs dry just so she can watch Gidget Meets The Wolfman. Besides, the guys had paid admission to a safe place to make out instead of risking being bushwhacked while parked on a lonely country road. No one watched the movie.

They could have shown three hours of Army training films on how to clean mud off combat boots and ninety percent of the patrons wouldn't have noticed. Unlike today's films, the hottest flicks starred such personalities as Audie Murphy and Elvis Presley. The closest we came to raw sex on the screen was Gabby Hayes wearing long underwear, cowboy boots, and a gun belt. We saw more gore from road kill than anything produced in Hollywood. The real action took place in the cars. As soon as it got dark, the place looked like La Belles Pleasure Palace on double green stamp night. Windows rolled up and steamed over, with heads barely visible above door sills and an occasional giggle as the only sign of life.

The guys never missed the opportunity to take a date to the latest horror film. For instance, while watching I Was A Teenage Werewolf we would offer our shoulder as a safe haven, where our date could bury her face and scream when the creature attacked an innocent victim. Heh, heh. Of course, we were too dense to realize that the girls were also taking advantage of the situation by pretending to be frightened at the sight of Michael Landon turning into a bad tempered dog. I never understood why my date would feed me a knuckle sandwich when I got a little frisky, and then fold at the sight of Boris Karloff as Frankenstein. I was probably closer to a real wolf man than anything created in Hollywood.

On the other hand, Saturday night and a carload of dateless boys was a different matter. Plans were made to see a movie but only two would pay admission. The others were stuffed into the trunk, causing the already lowered car to almost drag its bumper as it approached the ticket booth. Grinning like Cheshire cats and with the front tires barely touching the ground, the person in the booth would eye the car like a guard suspecting the grinners of being dope peddlers crossing the border from Mexico. Without smiling, he would charge admission for two and remark, "Enjoy the movie – all of you."

Inside, the driver would warn the trunk felons to remain quiet until he could find a suitable spot to release them. Of course, if it was your turn in the trunk you could expect some harassment. The driver and passenger would delay your release with false warnings that a theatre guard was passing, or that the preview for Fabian Meets The Topless Waitress was showing and it wasn't fit for innocent eyes. Only when it became a matter of suffocation or permanent damage to the trunk lid were the prisoners released. The rest of the evening was spent making life miserable for everyone within a radius of 100 yards with loud comments about the movie or the real show in the other cars. Halfway through the movie the gate crashers would be sitting alone as everyone else moved to calmer waters.

A trip to the concession stand took on the appearance of a scene from the Keystone Kops as the crashers moved about in a flurry, pushing and shoving, whistling at chicks, and greeting friends. All this was considered socially acceptable behavior, because next week another group of dateless delinquents would take their place to harass the previous weeks crashers and their dates.

We were creating our own field of dreams: images that would reappear years later as hazy remembrances of one of the most cherished times of our lives. Totally unaware that we would eventually fade away as ghosts of the future, it was a great time to be alive and there would be no end to it. So, once in a while everyone can be excused for drifting back and reliving those moments. It helps us cope with the rigors of the real world and makes us wish for the return of drive-in theatres and cars with bigger trunks.

STRETCHING THE TRUTH

I paced nervously back and forth as the mechanic poked around under the hood and occasionally shook his head and made "tsk, tsk" sounds. If the problem proved to be any more complex than a mouse nest in the carburetor, I would have to will the thing to him for the cost of repairs. I didn't think he would be willing to wait until I collected an inheritance to get his payment. Sitting in a corner of the grungy garage in a rocking chair that looked like it was about the same age as its occupant, was an old man, rolling back and forth as he watched the proceedings. He noticed my concern, and apparently serving as the public relations manager for the business, motioned me over.

"You a fisherman?" he asked.

"Yeh, whenever I can sell enough pop bottles to buy a can of worms" I answered.

"Let me tell you what happened last week," he said. "I had a few on the stringer when I noticed a commotion in the water around my fish. I pulled the stringer out and found a snake trying to steal one of my bluegills. I jerked the critter off the fish, squeezed him until his mouth popped

42

open, poured a shot of my favorite brew down his throat and throwed him back in the river. He left so fast he kicked up a rooster tail in the water. About ten minutes later I felt a tug on my pant leg and when I looked down, there was that snake with a fish in its mouth. It dropped it, reared up about a foot, opened its mouth and went, "Ahh, Ahh." By the end of the day I had a pretty good mess of fish and one dead drunk snake. I been planning to take that snake to Alcoholics Anonymous but he's so good at ketchin' fish I just cain't force myself to do it."

I asked him what kind of snake it was. He said he didn't know, but if I was interested I could go to Puffy's Bar and Grill. "It hangs around the door bumming drinks when it isn't fishing with me." I figured I didn't have to go to Puffy's to find the local reptile.

While I contemplated whether to tip the old huckster a quarter or simply tip him over in his chair, the mechanic announced that my engine had indeed been made into a condo by a roaming rodent. He gave me a home repair kit consisting of a piece of cheese and a mouse trap.

"If the car starts missing out again, put a fresh piece of cheese in the trap. If that doesn't work, I'd suggest you get a cat to help you with your tune-up."

I had asked for it. Any teenager with a flat top haircut, tightly pegged pants and zits who stumbled into Bucks Garage with a mouse nest in his engine is a target for every toothless, tobacco spitting liar in the country. I liked to think teens aren't that gullible, but for five bucks (the cost of being de-moused) it was great entertainment. As I drove home with the aroma of frying mouse droppings wafting through the heater, I considered what causes a storyteller to stretch the truth, especially when it came to us poor, "No kidding?", impressionable young people. Most of the tall tales I was subjected to, and I suppose it was because so many truth stretchers indulged in it, was about fishing. Ninety percent of the hogwash concerned either big fish, lots of fish, or the methods used to catch fish. For instance, a neighbor who was famous for his fish stories told of his most recent trip to the local river. He had encountered such a number of log sized denizens that he could have walked across the river on their backs and never have gotten more than the soles of his boots wet. The longer he talked the bigger the fish got and the more of them there were. "These things were eight feet long" he declared. When questioned about the brand of his liquor and the quantity he had consumed, he became indignant and then hostile, and accused us of calling him a liar. My Dad, who had been listening to him with quiet dignity, finally said, "You expect me to listen to you tell us there are fish in that river big enough to swallow a canoe and believe it when the biggest thing I've seen wasn't large enough to pull a rat on water ski's?"

"I'm telling the truth," he said. "You could put a saddle on any of 'em and ride it. At this point, all he had to say was that he had indeed saddled one and rode it downstream to the Ohio river and Dad would have hung him from the nearest tree. I, being a little more gullible, decided if there was even the slightest chance that what he said was true, my future fishing tools would consist of a shotgun and a harpoon. After all, this guy was an adult and if you couldn't trust a grown man, who could you trust?

Everyone is gullible, some more than others, but until a person is old enough to belly up to the bar, he or she depends on what they hear from adults as gospel. That is until some adults start talking about their dogs. Then, some credibility gaps begin to appear, because most kids are early experts on dogs. One favorite is about a dog that finds its way home from hundreds of miles away after enduring terrible hardships. These yarn spinners had apparently been watching too,many episodes of Lassie because most of the dogs I've known couldn't find their way home from next door unless they had a fishing line tied to their collar and were reeled in every night. I began to wonder about Dad's choice of friends, when after trying to swallow the big fish stories, another of his cronies told about his Irish Setter that preferred fishing over hunting. By now my skepticism was growing and I began rolling up my pant legs.

With a straight face, he began. "He'd stand on the bow of the boat with his tail sticking straight out behind him and watch the water ahead. If he wanted a turn, either right or left, his tail would swing in that direction. Whenever he spotted one big enough to mess with, his tail would shoot up like a flagpole and he'd go on point. All I had to do was drop the bait just off the end of his nose and Wham, I'd have the fish."

By then my nose was beginning to bleed as I asked him if the dog had any preference to the type of fish he pointed.

"I could tell what kind of fish it was by his tail. If it was a catfish he'd swing his tail in a circle. For a perch he'd move it up and down like a pump handle. If it was a carp he'd tuck his tail between his legs, curl his lips back and stick out his tongue."

He didn't know how close I was to pulling the trigger as I asked, "Do you still have this dog?"

"Naw, one day he got so excited when he spotted a six foot channel cat that he began to wag his tail and I tried to steer the boat according to his directions. Threw him overboard and he drowned. I didn't know he couldn't swim."

That did it. I pulled the trigger. I could swallow most of it, but who had ever heard of a six foot catfish?

COTTON CANDY AND PRINCESS PISTACHIO

For weeks prior to its appearance, signs and posters tacked to light poles and hung from the sides of buildings announced the coming event. The blaring promises of mystery and fun would feature colorful and comical renditions of The Dog Faced Boy and the world's fattest man surrounded by such temptations as, "See The Biggest Little Midway In The Universe," and, Ride Colossus – Tallest Ferris Wheel In The World." In smaller print was what Dad referred to as the hootchie-kootchie show. "See Princess Pistachio Perform Her Famous Dance Of The Seven Camels." In even smaller letters was, "Must Be 18 To Enter."

The carnival was coming to town.

No other event held such sway over our imaginations, or inspired in us such fascination as the appearance of one of these assemblages of ratty old tents, noise and confusion, bright lights, time worn rides that creaked and rumbled like ancient steam engines, and workers who looked like bathing was something to be avoided at all costs. Our normally uncooperative dispositions would change from whining at the smallest chores to volunteering to tear down the garage and build a new one if the wage scale was to be equal to our needs for those few days of pleasure. Before the appearance of the posters we couldn't hang onto a quarter long enough for it to fall through a hole in our pocket. Now, with the lure of cotton candy and Tilt-A-Whirls, we wouldn't give a nickel to watch a dog climb a tree. Every penny was pinched and closely guarded.

The big day finally arrived and, as if by the wave of a magicians wand, the field that had been vacant the night before was transformed into a sea of activity and sounds as riggers struggled to erect rides and unfold midway gaming booths. Hanging around on the fringes, we marveled at the language as grimy carny workers broadened our not so meager knowledge of profanity by yelling at each other over the squeal of rusty bolts and snorting generators. Here was romance.

We figured the average carny worker weighed no more than 160 pounds of hardened muscle, but when the thick layers of grunge on skin and clothing was figured in, they probably topped the scales at 180 pounds or more. To us, dirt was an ingredient to be worn with pride and here were our heroes, stalwart champions of filth and leaders of the anti-establishment movement. Thereafter, as we cringed at taking a bath, visions of these magnificent symbols of crud filled us with envy.

Decrepit camper trailers with license plates from such exotic places as Florida, Georgia, and Alabama lined one end of the field and served as living quarters for these modern day gypsies: people who paid no taxes and answered to no one but the owners of this mobile junk yard. Their life was reflected in weary faces and tired bodies, accompanied by a generally sullen attitude that set them apart from the rubes who would pay for next week's groceries with their quarters and dollars.

Daylight revealed the truth that darkness cloaked. Once brightly colored canvas tents stood faded and torn. Paint peeled from everything. Duct tape and bailing wire held most of the display together and made the entire scene look like a major explosion in a huge scrap heap. As darkness came, the scene changed as brightly colored lights transformed the mess into a fairyland of flawless perfection. A dozen tunes from scratchy records blared over loud speakers while midway hawkers shouted their enticements to "Step right up here, ladies and gentlemen! Break three balloons and win your choice of the top shelf!" Or, "How about you, little lady? You look like you can handle a gun. Shoot out the star and win a big, cuddly teddy bear!" A mixture of the aroma of greasy hamburgers and hot dogs mingling with cotton candy hung in the air like cheap perfume. It just didn't get any better than this.

On one memorable visit by these purveyors of thrills and pleasures, myself and another numbskull decided to experience two of life's biggest moments – a ride on the Loop-O-Plane and our first exposure to raw sex – or any sex for that matter. Finding Princess Pistachio's tent, we stood at a distance and cast covert glances at the gaudily painted signs hanging from the front entrance. Of special interest was the small one that read, "Must Be 18 To Enter." Since neither of us could work up even a shadow of facial hair through a combined effort and thus pass for the legal age, we figured we had a better chance of joining the Army than getting through that opening. The only option was to sneak in.

Slipping behind the tent we cased it for a way to slip in under a flap. Loosely driven pegs allowed the tent to be lifted far enough to crawl under and we soon stood in the dim light, undetected among the taller men around us. Up to that time our only experience with bare flesh had been through the courtesy of Sears and Roebuck. That night we were to discover why certain foundation garments are necessary.

When the tent was sufficiently full of sweaty farmers and cigar smoke, the princess made her appearance. If this was a princess, her father, the king, must have ruled over a country devoid of bathtubs or dietary concerns. The costume she wore, if it could be called that, looked like a grass sack that had hosted a fight between two wildcats. Bands of gaudy beads hung from her shoulders and waist as she struggled to maintain her balance on spike heels that sunk into the soft ground.

Chewing gum, she began swaying and bouncing to what we decided must be her national anthem but sounded suspiciously like the latest from Grandpa Jones and the Smokey Mountain Boys. Aghast, we watched as she removed the grass sack while the farmers hooted and hollered. So that's what an overweight, underwashed female looks like. Five minutes of bump and grind later, our introduction to the physical aspects of the fair sex was over. Exiting through our private entrance, we agreed to stick to hunting and fishing for another twenty years and leave girl chasing to our older brothers.

Standing in line at the dreaded Loop-O-Plane, quarters clutched in sweaty palms, we awaited our turn to replace the hapless, screaming victims now trapped in the thing. Training copperheads to sit up and beg seemed tame by comparison, but neither of us would admit fear. Unfortunately, I had stocked up on an ample supply of junk food earlier and was ignorant of the effect on my stomach when it's subjected to anything other than resting comfortably above my feet. Locked into the wire cage, we began whirling and spinning as the demonic thing looped us thirty feet above the ground. Time seemed to stop as each revolution brought me closer to a complete severance of diplomatic relations with my stomach. Finally, the gremlins running the thing stopped us, hanging upside down at the very top while he loaded a new batch of victims. At that point I lost the gastrointestinal war and cleared out everyone within a twenty foot radius on the ground below. Later, I slunk around the midway like a weasel, hoping no one who still had remnants of a foot long hot dog clinging to their shirt would recognize me.

So much for sex and bravery. The only thing left to complete the evening would have been a big cigar behind the Port-A-Potties. It wouldn't have changed my already light pastel green complexion a single shade and we could have bragged about graduating with honors from a crash course in socially unacceptable practices.

After a week of unbridled fun and sin, the grungy group would swing into action, collapsing tents, dismantling rides, and loading trailers. By Sunday morning, the field would be bare, with only empty cups, carcasses of broken balloons and sticky cotton candy paper cones left as evidence that these phantoms of mystery and pleasure had been there. Our world would return to the everyday humdrum of self-made entertainment that was typical of small town life.

Somewhere, suspended in the space-time continuum, are ghostly forms of weather worn, faded tents, rotund princesses, and a midway sparkling with colorful lights and greasy roustabouts shouting profanities. Squeals and screams are mingling with the rumble of aging Tilt-A-Whirls and Loop-O-Planes, and when I die, the first place I'm heading for is there, with a pocket full of quarters. No doubt it will be necessary to push the down button on the elevator to get there, but where else could it be?

KITTY

I have a philosophy that every life is like an imperfect gossamer thread woven into the tapestry of time by a careless weaver, but destined to be worn as a shroud in the end.

If a life thread could be followed, it would dip and swerve, crossing the course of other threads, briefly flowing parallel with some, and in all likelihood be joined by another as two lives unite for the greatest journey in the universe.

Like marathon runners, we leap into life with a burst of speed, enjoying our youth and vigor, exploring optional routes, shrugging off those blind alleys that leave us with our noses flattened against immovable walls and savoring those that lead to satisfaction. We are immortal: time means only here and now, and Peter Pan and Tinker Bell are real.

Years pass as we slow our pace and examine the endless paths available to us with greater care, choosing only those that seem to offer fewer pitfalls and greater comfort and security. Awareness of the finite length of our existence begins to whisper "caution" into our subconscious ear.

Finally, we walk toward our destiny with hands in pockets, either satisfied with a look over our shoulder at where we've been, or filled with a sense of loss for where we haven't. Feelings of contentment, regret, sadness – all give meaning to the saying, "If I had known I was going to live this long, I would have taken better care of myself."

I haven't got my hands in my pockets yet, but occasionally I stop long enough to re-tie my shoelaces. Recently, during one of these rest periods, I thought back on some of the people with whom my lifeline had tangled and realized that in my rush to get here, I had sprinted past the wealth that sat along the road.

Impetuous youth and its ability to turn a brain into something that had no control over anything but eating, chasing the opposite sex and drag racing had robbed me of the pleasure of experiencing and sharing in other lives – older lives that could have led me back in time to adventures that seemed like transparent, meaningless events in history books, written about a bunch of supposedly fictional dead people.

If Abraham Lincoln had suddenly materialized, I and many of my peers would have attended his speeches only if required to do so, but within fifteen minutes we would have been edging toward the exits. Our philosophy (myself and the rest of the delinquents I hung around with) was, "You've got plenty of time, but don't waste it on anything that goes less than 100 miles per hour or anyone who was born before Twinkies were invented."

Anyone who wanted a parking space at any local hangout had only to pull in with the radio blasting out a tune by Lawrence Welk. It was a guarantee that you'd be alone before the second stanza of his theme song was finished. Although I wasn't aware of it at the time, I had the pleasure of sharing my life line for a brief moment with a man who today I know so little about, but who left me with a permanent regret for not having sat beside the road with him for just a little while longer. So old that moss was growing on his east side, Kitty (having never asked, I assumed that was his nickname) lived alone in a small two room cabin overlooking White River, just over the bluff from the house we had just moved into.

Since access to the river and the boat docks was down his walk, and having turned over a number of outhouses on people over 50, I cautiously made his acquaintance with the thought in mind that old age carried with it a hostility toward zit-plagued teenagers. Faced with the choices of either sneaking past or knocking on his door and asking permission to use the path, I chose the latter, fully expecting to be whacked with a cane and be called a young whippersnapper. Instead, I was invited in to visit for a spell.

His living room and kitchen reeked heavily of old wood, peeling linoleum, and years of accumulation of cigarette smoke. The furniture consisted of two ratty old rocking chairs, a 1950's style dinette set and a four-burner kitchen stove. An open door revealed a small bedroom with an iron bed and a small chest-of-drawers, both of which would have had an antique dealer reaching for his check book.

This first encounter consisted of the two rockers squeaking and cracking as I answered questions about myself while Kitty chain smoked Pall Malls, lighting one off another as they burned perilously close to his yellow, nicotine stained fingers. Permission to come and go as I pleased was granted and during the ensuing months I would occasionally run errands to the grocery store for him or sit and listen as he rocked and quietly spun stories about his past.

Here was someone who had been born before Custer gained notoriety at Little Big Horn and who, in his late teens had ridden shotgun on the last stagecoaches in the southwest before they were replaced by the railroads. Vowing that "if you cain't beat 'em, join 'em", he then worked laying rails while living in the wide open towns that sprung up along the routes.

Hollywood had formed my images of this era and I asked him questions about outlaws, Indians, and shootouts at high noon. He would chuckle and tell me how it really was: that life could be risky on a Saturday night, but that you stood a better chance of sinking out of sight in the perennially muddy streets and drowning, than being arrowed by an Indian or shot in a bar room brawl. Life was hard but rarely as romantic as the dime store novels depicted.

Eventually, his stories faded in my mind into a fog of antiquated tales that I tired of – partly because I didn't want to believe that John Wayne was a fake - and partly because I was convinced that this kindly, shrunken old man could not possibly have ever been anything but an old man living in a dream world of his own creation. Subconsciously, I felt that the world before my birth was just a myth created to entertain me with stories of cowboys and Indians.

Years passed, I got married, moved away, and Kitty was forgotten. One day on a visit home, my mother casually said, "Oh, by the way, Kitty died yesterday." The reality that his lifeline had faded to an end and that I hadn't had the chance to say good-bye opened up a void created by my eventual indifference to a continued sharing of the past and present with someone who could have enriched my life immeasurably.

What I wouldn't give to once again sit in those old rockers, listening to them creak, smelling the aroma of musty linoleum and say, "Talk to me Kitty. Now I'm listening."

TO DOMESTICATE AND GROW A WILD CROP

Anyone who manages to survive the first few years of life is either very lucky or has been locked in a cellar and fed through a hole in the door. Pure, dumb luck had been my saving grace, but now, I was faced with adapting to certain responsibilities reserved for a more mature person at the age of 12. However, one of those symbols of manhood seemed to be unobtainable and I was determined to right that wrong.

A beard is a sign of manhood achieved
The symbol of hormones gone wild
It delights the boy who's always believed
Such growth marks the loss of the child

But why do we comb and grub and scrape
To cultivate such wiry strands
When we ignore the fact we can't escape
It grows wild on the back of our hands

For as long as I could remember, my father sported what my mother called his "go to hell" moustache. A thin ribbon of wiry hair, it rested on his upper lip like an undernourished wooly worm. On those rare occasions when he tired of combing half his breakfast out of it, or when it blocked his blowing a fly off the end of his nose, he would sharpen his straight razor and remove it. Normally, this would result in two distinct reactions from the rest of the family. Us kids would comment on how he looked so much better with an upper lip that looked like it was now three inches below his nose and mom would seem less reluctant to kiss him goodbye in the morning. I often thought that smooching a moustache would be like sticking your face into a blackberry bush, but since I hadn't any immediate plans to be kissing girls I couldn't wait until my facial follicles began producing something other than zits.

By the age of 12 I began to wonder if I was doomed to suffer forever with hairless cheeks and lips. About twice a year I would lather up and remove what growth there was along with half the top layer of skin. Six months later, a new crop with the density and texture of peach fuzz would have developed. That is, if a strong light were held on it and someone else swore it was there. Meanwhile, dad continued to grow and remove his with no apparent concern about it re-appearing whenever he chose, while I had to resort to a false lip hair piece. The only problem with this was the plastic horn rimmed glasses and the big rubber nose that came with it. By the age of 18 I was beginning to see some results. I was shaving every other week and doing it with the latest from the world of advanced technology. Dad bought an electric razor and the sound of the little whiner could be heard every morning as he prepared to go to work. Most members of the male gender who used the first examples of electric facial hair control devices will attest to the fact that the mechanical sciences had a long way to go to perfect these fuzz whackers. After a few uses the blades would dull to the sharpness of a cold chisel, resulting in more whiskers being pulled out than cut. Frequently, I would awake and lie in bed waiting for the start of the usual morning ritual.

While trying to trim the weeds around his garden, dad would miscalculate and drag a few hairs out of his moustache with the little buzz saw.

"EEYOW – THIS DODDURN, DADGUMMED – WHERE"S MY SAFETY RAZOR"?

A few moments of silence would follow.

"EEYOW – AMELIA, HAVE YOU BEEN SHAVING YOUR LEGS WITH MY RAZOR AGAIN"?

I still don't understand how the hair on a lady's legs can dull a razor that is sharp enough to cut the nucleus of an atom.

At breakfast, his face looked like it had been attacked by a weed whacker, with little pieces of toilet paper covering the spots where excessive skin had been removed. What with my typical adolescent crop of pimples, and considering the amount of top soil it seemed necessary to remove when harvesting the crop, I decided to wait until something substantial appeared before sharpening the axe.

By the age of 22 I was apparently not putting enough fertilizer on the lawn. Shaving only every other day and soon to be married, I was sick of being asked if I was still using the cat to lick off my growth. I reasoned that facial hair was like weeds: the more you agitate them, the faster they grow, so I shaved every day until a shadow finally began to form on my upper lip. Glory Hallelujah! It was time to try for that most hallowed symbol of manhood, a moustache and beard.

Two weeks later my face looked like the return of life to the desert floor 10 years after the first atomic blast. Little patches of scraggly hair were scattered at random on my acreage with no signs that the bare spots would ever support a paying crop. No amount of grooming would convince it to do anything other than stick straight out at odd angles like a hairdo on a mangy dog. When my wife Judy finally requested I wear a sign saying, "I Bathe Daily", it fell under the scythe.

Years later I managed to produce a moustache that still graces my lip. Once, in a moment of weakness, I shaved it off and spent the next three weeks in seclusion until it sprouted again. I looked like a pouting Stan Laurel.

Why do some men work so hard at grooming facial hair? Very simple. It allows us to fit into whatever social order we choose. On one of my visits to a news office, I noticed Jeff, the publisher, had removed his moustache. Looking ten years younger, he would no longer be accepted by the motorcycling fraternity.

Instead, he was then free to cruise the strip and hang out at the local teen hot spots. In the past, the strength and prominence of Vikings and pirates was judged by their facial decorations. Eric The Red, Blackbeard The Pirate, and Bluebeard were notorious for their ferocity and nefarious deeds, although old Bluebeard apparently had a kinky hairdresser.

A hairy man has always been a symbol of strength and integrity as evidenced by the number of historically prominent men who sported beards. On the other hand, maybe these same people were pulling a classic cover-up. The old saying is, "A good growth of honeysuckle can hide even the ugliest board fence." Or perhaps for those frustrated gardeners like me who can't grow horseweed in a compost heap, it's a way of showing the world we can produce something other than bad breath.

A word of advice for those who are considering some form of hairy landscaping. Decide what you want and then practice on the family dog. It will save you a lot of frustration and give you an idea what you will look like in six months.

FROG ANATOMY AND PSYCHOTIC RATS

During my first 12 years in school, I seemed to be the focal point of attempts by the teaching profession to achieve a first by educating a concrete block.

By the third grade, my reputation as the kid whose vocabulary was limited to "Huh" and "I dunno" was legend. I began to suspect that I was special when on the first day of each subsequent school year, as I walked into class, the teacher would lay his or her head on the desk and begin sobbing, "Oh NONONONONONO."

Biology was an especially favorite subject of mine, and a landmark time for the rest of the school. Shortly after we had studied frog anatomy by dissection, the school paper printed a special edition with the following headlines emblazoned across the feature article:

"You Know Who Says YUCK!"

Below this was, "Frog Fillet Freaks Frosh!"

The storyline followed with, "In an unprecedented move of expanded vocabulary, a student known as "The Slug" voiced his opinion of the interior of a former member of the lily pad set. This unexpected outburst caught his classmates and a few more on the sidewalk below the window where he hung to regurgitate by surprise. When asked at what point in the surgery his victim changed from fried frog legs to scalpel induced road kill, he replied, "I dunno." The entire school will be watching anxiously for next semester's reaction to snake disection."

Upon graduation from high school, I had to decide whether to continue on to college and a doctorate in frog and snake surgery, or to pursue some other, possibly more lucrative field. After all, I reasoned, it would be difficult to change old habits, from gig and hoe to scalpel and sutures. It was time to investigate other avenues.

I considered nuclear physics but discarded the idea when I found that no home study courses in the subject were available. I had envisioned a home study package arriving complete with an economy sized cyclotron and a gram of pure plutonium.

Armed with an HSC (Home Study Course) PHD, I would face the world with the first accelerated neutron particle bomb and never again be forced to peel the overcoat off a reluctant snake or have to remove the spleen from a toad. Browsing through the list of Do-It-Yourself Degrees, I found the next best thing. Electronics.

Here was a technology that, even though it was a poor substitute for a neutron bomb, offered vast potential. I would invent a molecular disintegrator and vaporize the local selective service office!

A few weeks later a large package arrived containing study and instruction manuals and an assortment of strange looking electronic components. I was to start by constructing such simple items as an oscilloscope and a transistorized voltmeter.

Two months later as I tried to convince the EMF that it was alright to polarize the 3.2 ohm TRVM, the possibilities of a disintegrator began to dim along with my hopes of being passed over by the draft board. There was only one logical endeavor left to pursue. The noble and lucrative profession of human psychology.

After checking the curriculum of a local university, I enrolled in Psych 101, purchased the necessary texts and reported for the first class. Sigmund Freud, move over.

Our professor, a rather nervous man, introduced himself and began outlining the study plan for the coming semester.

"Good evening class. My name is Mr. Silverstein. Please feel free to call me Mr. Silverstein. Hee, hee, just a little joke." I mentally filed away the distance to the nearest exit.

He continued: "We will spend the first half of the course studying the basis of conditioned responses to external stimuli. You will learn why your parents moved the day after you left for college and left no forwarding address. You see, you are the external stimulus to their bank account. Hee, hee." I began to consider whether to bring a corn knife or a shotgun to the next class for protection. His next announcement shook my foundation:"The last half of the semester will be spent studying actual conditioned responses in rat lab." I sat bolt upright. Rat lab? With a sinking feeling in my stomach I held up my hand.

"Yes Mr., uh – slug? Do you have a question?"

"Yes, sir. Why do you call it rat lab?"

"We will instill actual conditioned responses in laboratory rats to demonstrate those same responses in humans," he said. "The class will be divided into pairs of ladies and gentlemen. This way, the ladies will have one of you brave gentlemen to handle your respective rats."

In a cold sweat I asked, "Could you pair me with a lady who has had some time working in a city dump? I just got out of an institution that required being on a first name basis with various reptiles, and I hadn't planned on graduating to rats so soon."

The first weeks dragged by until, finally the big day arrived when we were introduced to our patients. The professor, in a move to assure us of the docility of the critters, stuck his hand into a cage to bring one out and was promptly bitten on a finger. That did it! I reached into my briefcase and brought out a large trap and a box of D-Con. As the professor wrapped a Band-Aid on his finger, my partner informed me that if I refused to handle the little assassin, we could both kiss this course good-bye. At fifty bucks a credit hour, I told her that I would put tennis shoes on a gorilla before I would let a rat stand in the way of our getting a higher education.

The next few weeks proved interesting as we taught our subject to respond to the ringing of a bell for a drink of water. In fact, we grew quite fond of Leroy and finally made an offer to purchase him. We envisioned ourselves prancing into the center ring as spotlights illuminated our flashing costumes. Leroy, resplendent in tights and a cape, would be billed as the world's only rat powered high wire act.

Fame and fortune would be ours. Unfortunately, during one class session, Leroy got his tongue caught in the mechanical water dipper and thereafter, refused all offers to quench his thirst. By the end of classes he was sullen and withdrawn, as well as dehydrated. No matter how hard we coaxed and pleaded he remained cowered in a corner, totally oblivious to the bell. In a final desperate attempt at regaining his confidence, we requested and were refused the use of electric shock therapy on him. As we watched our plans for fame and fortune, as well as an "A" in the course go down the toilet, I recalled an appropriate saying that summed up the situation:

"You can lead a rat to water, but you can't make him drink."

FAIRY TALES AND YOUTHFUL INNOCENCE

(If you don't believe in something you can't see, how can you explain a chigger bite?)

On either side of the road and stretching into the distance, the mist and rain veiled the color of the trees and blended them into an endless display of nature's finest fall splendor. Oranges, reds and yellows were softened into a collage of the different types of trees that complimented each other in their finery. As we drove, exclamations of, "Oh, Wow, look at that one" and frequent ooh's and ahh's were common as one of the finest autumns in memory flowed by. Finally, someone inevitably gave the credits for such grandeur to old you-know-who. "Mother Nature has sure outdone herself this year."

Who is Mother Nature? Every time I hear her mentioned, I envision a matronly mother figure wearing granny glasses, sitting on a stump and leaning back against a tree with a jug of home-made brew in one hand and a half-full wine glass in the other while she barks orders at a bunch of overworked forest elves who scurry around flinging rainbow hued fairy dust on trees.

"Mother Nature your foot," I replied. "She's nothing but a soak. Those little guys with curly toed shoes do all the work while she lays around and criticizes their work. For once, why don't you give credit where credit's due." Silence followed as everyone stared at me as though a snow snake had just popped out of my shirt pocket. "Well, it's true," I continued. "Do you think one old lady could do all this work by herself?" One of the back seat passengers produced a crucifix and pressed it to her breast while mumbling something in Latin.

I realized I had committed one of the great transgressions by ridiculing a mythological character that we had been taught from childhood was real and that represented all that is good and wholesome in the world. Of course, such phantoms don't represent the same image to everyone. As we continued our sightseeing tour, I shut the pain of the burn from the crucifix out of my mind by thinking back on other unseen entities and their impact on my young life.

Naturally, the king of them all was the grand old symbol of gift giving, the master of ceremonies of the polar regions, the red suited, chubby little fellow with a rather unkempt beard who spent two weeks out of every year sitting in a little shack on the courthouse lawn: Santa Claus.

Up to the age of seven or eight, I believed the North Pole was overrun with little people wearing pointed little hats with a dingleball hanging from it, who slaved year-round to make bicycles, B-B guns, and Lionel train sets. However, the bubble developed a slow leak when one of my gifts was turned over and I read on the back, "Made In Japan." Did the old gent have a branch office in Tokyo?

The truth finally dawned on me the next year when the rubber band holding Santa's beard in place broke while I sat on his lap. Oh, the cruelty of larcenous adults.

The next idol to hit the dirt was the one my parents used occasionally to convince me that a trip to the dentist would be rewarded handsomely. The idea here was to place a fallen biscupid under your pillow at bed time, and the next morning it would have been purchased at a fair market value by this wisp of the night. My vision of the Tooth Fairy bore a remarkable resemblance to Mortimer Snerd, complete with a long hooked nose and eyelids that made his eyes look like windows with the shades half drawn. The idea of this nerdy gnome roaming around my bed in the wee hours gave me little comfort, but greed always won out.

The big crash came when a tooth fell out without any coaxing and I placed it under my pillow without informing my parents. The next morning the exchange had not been made and I lodged a complaint with the management. As gently as possible, they informed me of the truth. Heartbroken at the demise of another legend, I was nonetheless grateful for not following through with a plan to pull a few extra teeth from the dog. So what would have been wrong with a little larceny? After all, since the mutt loved peanut butter and bread, he didn't need all those teeth anyway.

At one time or another, in every kid's life, there enters that most dreaded of specters, the Boogey Man. Here was evil incarnate. All that was needed to stop a temper tantrum was the threat of a spoonful of Dr. Drakes Elixer or an invitation for a nocturnal visit by the Boogey Man. Tears and wails were replaced by wide-eyed frantic looks and a request for another helping of sardine and turnip salad.

For me, the passing of years hasn't dispelled the reality of such a creature. Now, he's no longer a monster that emits growls and rumblings from the shadows of the night. He quit his old job and is now working for the IRS.

Of all the myths that should have tipped us off to our being the butt of adult humor, the Easter Bunny was the one. We were led to believe that on Easter, a large rabbit, who had spent considerable time coloring (bunny) eggs, hopped around during the night delivering said eggs to every kid in the world. Why? Agreed, we arose eagerly on the appointed morning and flew around the house and yard looking for our share of these less than delectable prizes, but for what purpose? Not only did those things look suspiciously like they came, not from a rabbit, but from our chicken coop, they also stuck to the roof of your mouth like any ordinary hard boiled egg. Not until they were mixed with marshmallow chicks and chocolate bunnies did they take on any degree of significance. When questioned about their origin, my parents stopped just short of claiming they were laid by a rabbit. However, for years I thought those cute little bunnies came from calcium enclosures.

When things got rough, the one we knew we could depend on was our Fairy Godmother. Here was someone who would stick by us through thick and thin and who watched over us while we slept to keep the Boogey Man off our backs. She overlooked our transgressions and understood why we felt it necessary to pelt someone with the rotten eggs we found in the barn. To me she was best described as follows:

Nighttime fears in childhood years,
Are soothed by she who whispers,
Soft calming words into our ears,
My Fairy Godmother,
Ah, but could I have kiss'd her.

FRANKENSTEIN '37
MEETS TERMINATOR '95

(It's getting pretty bad when the scariest costumes at Halloween seem like prom clothes when compared to what comes out of Hollywood the rest of the year.)

From under the sink came a barrage of profanity that had the dog cowering in the corner with his tail tucked between his legs. "How in the #%$*^# can anyone get this much crud on themselves from water pipes?" I shouted. "We're not pumping oil here. These pipes are supposed to be carrying water." Struggling from under the blasted thing I yelled, "And, why don't these #%&^$%# pipes go back together the way they came apart?" I finished off with a blast that caused the dog to whimper and start clawing at the door while eyeing me like a snake watching a gardener armed with a hoe. Finally, the job was done. There was still one small leak of about two gallons a minute (that's why they make buckets) and I had only six pieces of pipe left over. It had taken quite a bit of ingenuity, but I managed to move things around and remove that big, funny looking bend in the drain pipe just under the sink. Now, I can flush anything up to the size of a softball down the drain and not worry about clogs. After a hard day of home repairs, it was time for a little entertainment. "Honey, let's go to a movie," I suggested. Judy agreed and soon we were seated in the theatre, popcorn in hand and ready to watch that highly acclaimed silver screen smash, Starship Troopers. Touted for its special effects, I nonetheless expected it to rank on about the same level as a Saturday morning with the Power Rangers. For the first twenty minutes I wasn't disappointed, but halfway through I understood why it had an "R" rating. Whoever thought this one up is probably working part time in entertainment while spending the rest of his day pulling wings off bugs and dropping buckets of hot tar off overpasses. To say that Judy is a "little" sensitive to violence in movies is like saying that one could get a "little" wet falling into a lake. By the time the really hairy scenes flashed on the screen, she had latched onto my arm like bark on a beech tree and was occasionally helping the good guys out by shouting, "Watch out behind you."After struggling unsuccessfully to break her hold on my now lifeless limb due to a lack of blood flow, I thought of a similar scene years ago. We had treed a coon up a skinny, 15-foot tall tree and were attempting to shake it out. With all four feet wrapped firmly around the trunk, the coon held on like a fly on a hood ornament. We couldn't have pried it off with a crowbar. Faced with the same situation as the coon and with my fingers numb, I finally told her that if she didn't release me soon, I'd make her stay and watch the thing over again. That did it. She slumped down and proceeded to pull little tufts of stuffing out of her seat while muttering something about being married to a science fiction nut.

Driving home as Judy sat beside me making little "phfft, phfft" noises and trying to control the tic in her right eye, I thought back in the movies we shuddered at as kids. The monsters of that era are laughable now, but to us Frankenstein and the Wolfman represented the ultimate in terrifying entertainment. The scarred character in elevator shoes, electrodes protruding from his temples and neck, and wearing too-small clothing symbolized the thing hanging around in every dark corner, just waiting for the chance to catch a ten-year old kid and skin it. As far as we were concerned, the monster had itself made up to look like Boris Karloff when it went out into public life, but turned itself back into its gruesome self when making movies. However, old Franky was a pansy when compared to the ultimate horror, the epitome of things unholy, the Wolfman. Here was evil incarnate. After watching this master of transformation perform his nasty deeds, and if the walk home was after dark, we were as nervous as fuse testers in a dynamite factory. Every dark shadow held a hairy face and a mouthful of very sharp dental work. The idea that a middle-aged, rather meek guy who looked like a cab driver (Lon Chaney) could turn into such a thing meant that anyone with a five o'clock shadow was definitely not to be trusted.

As the years passed, it took more than a chubby lycanthrope or a stiff-legged corpse with a wardrobe problem to scare us. We had moved on to bigger and better ghouls. Mindless axe murderers, sophisticated Draculas and horrible alien monsters drew us to drive-ins like carp to a doughball. Although we no longer believed in spooks and werewolves, we soon discovered that these low budget flicks were a blessing in disguise on Saturday night dates. We would have passed up free tickets to a barn fire to take a date to watch mutant sea monsters suck the brains out of innocent victims. When the going got rough, we were there, selflessly offering ourselves as a stalwart oasis of comfort to our terrified date who would cling to us like moss on a rock. Of course, she wasn't half as scared as she pretended to be, but Michael Landon as a teenage werewolf offered a good excuse for "exchanging oxygen".

As we have become more sophisticated in our desires for movie entertainment, so has our demand for realism increased. Ever ready to accommodate us, Hollywood, with the help of computer generated graphics, has been churning out films that would have caused a ten-year old in my time to refuse to leave home for fifteen years.

For instance, the plot of the movie we watched was a futuristic interplanetary war against a race of BUGS. Not your ordinary garden variety, grind-'em under your heel bugs, but thanks to computer imaging, bugs that would cause even the Orkin Man to think twice before tackling them. The special effects were indeed outstanding, but so were the claw marks I still carry from sitting next to a woman who has nightmares from watching Bud Abbot and Lou Costello Meet Frankenstein.

After such tidbits, I wonder when Hollywood will come up with a remake of Bambi, where with the price of admission, the moviegoers will be issued a bow and a quiver of arrows. At the right moment, everyone can unleash a fusillade of arrows at the screen and pincushion the little fellow as he talks to Thumper. Free passes to the next feature would be awarded to anyone who nails the rabbit. Now, that's entertainment.

YOUR BASIC INTELLECTUAL AND COMIC STRIPS

(There was a time when reading the Sunday funnies was for light hearted entertainment and relaxation.. Today, a degree in political science is needed just to understand them.)

Puzzled, I re-read Doonesbury for the third time, trying to grasp the punch line and relate it to the situation between Duke and his Chinese girlfriend. To further confuse the issue, the guy who always wears the football helmet would occasionally intercede with a profound statement and drop another bale of hay in my already overfilled barn.

I finally gave up and moved on to the next comic strip with a firm determination to grasp the meaning of the dialogue. Ha! It happened to be one of the newer strips called "Bliss" where a young married couple, apparently just graduated from "Yuppie University", communicates with each other in a language that can be understood by less than a tenth of the reading public. They banter back and forth in what I call 21st century techno-speak which, for those of my generation, might as well be Swahili. Strike two!

In desperation, and to prove to myself that I am of at least average intelligence, I moved on to "Dilbert". By the time I reached the third frame I was sobbing and unable to control my depression.

I am of below average intelligence. How can I expect to keep up with current events or decipher all those notices of major prizes we receive in the mail if I can't even understand these stupid comics. "I'm an old failure," I cried.

Judy threw a glass of cold water in my face to stop the hiccupping and then consoled me by reading "Garfield" while pointing to the corresponding frame. "You understand this, don't you?" she asked.

"Y-Y-Yes," I stuttered.

"Well then, just don't worry about trying to understand those modern message comics. They'll cause you to have nightmares and I'll have to strap you down in bed again."

"But, aren't they supposed to be humorous and make you laugh while you read them?"

"Not any more," she replied. Pointing to the first frame of "Dilbert", she quoted him as saying to his boss, "I need help on the assignment you said is a no-brainer."

In the next frame his boss replies. "It's easy. Just skip the interface design phase and make everything beige. You can't go wrong with beige."

My chin began to quiver again and my voice cracked as I said, "What does he mean by "interface design phase?"

"It means things that work together or interact," she said.

"See?" I wailed. "You can understand Dilbert and I can't."

With a sigh of resignation she looked at me with pity in her eyes and returned to reading "Jason Potter's Space Walk".

With the help of Beetle Bailey and Hagar The Horrible I finally calmed down enough to think things out in a rational manner. In general, comic strip characters have changed dramatically over the years, from buffoons, to modern swingers who keep us abreast of today's events in a satirical way. Since I prefer the old ways, I thought back on some of the strips we used to enjoy.

Not necessarily one of my favorites, but one that came to mind was Mandrake The Magician. This character in his traditional magicians garb and jaunty little moustache would "gesture hypnotically" and render his foes unable to flick a fly off their nose. To a kid he was immensely boring, but at least his plot and story line wasn't impossible to follow.

Another was Lil' Abner, with Daisy Mae, Mammy Yokum, Pappy Yokum, little critters called schmoos, and a diminutive character named Joe Sphlkxs (or something like that) who constantly had a small, black cloud hanging over his head.

As proof that we were no less receptive to the type of marketing hype that captures today's kids, a toy company started pushing schmoos, and the rush was on. If you didn't have a schmoo toy, you were a social outcast that lived in a tar paper shack with outdoor plumbing. Even parents were influenced by the characters in the strips as witnessed by mom who began ending her orders to us with, "Ah has spoken," a favorite line by Mammy Yokum. I saw little humor in it however, as it normally followed a directive to do something like, "Feed the hogs."

One of my all time favorites was Fearless Fosdick, a lame-brained detective who exhibited the intelligence of a beer can. Shootouts with the bad guys were common and invariably resulted in Fearless being fiiled with holes that allowed the reader to see daylight through him. Small tendrils of smoke curled out of them and the size of the hole depended on the caliber of the gun.

On many occasions, Fearless took on the appearance of a misshapen piece of smoking Swiss cheese, but he always rallied for the next week's adventure. It was great fun to see him stand with crossed eyes and his tongue sticking out of the corner of his mouth while smoke wisped out of a quarter-sized hole in his head. Boy, would the comic censor cops have a field day with that one today.

The forerunners of today's modern comics were Tumbleweeds and Bloom County. Tumbleweeds was honest humor in the form of a bachelor cowboy and a swayback horse being pursued by a buck-toothed, freckle-faced spinster, a grave digger named Claude Clay, flocks of philosophical Indians, and a knuckle dragging Indian oaf named Bucolic Buffalo. My favorite memory of this now defunct strip was Claude Clay standing in a half-dug grave singing:

Standing in the Quagmire
Working Up A Perspire
Lord, I'm gonna Expire
If I Don't Retire
Gravediggers Bluuuuues
It doesn't take much to keep me entertained.

Bloom County and its cousin, The Far Side, achieved the pinnacle of understandable adult oriented humor. Here, the warped minds of Breathed and Larson demonstrated how pudgy penguins, intellectual cockroaches, a hairball spitting, dope-headed cat, groupy bears, boneless chickens, and an amoeba dressed in a sarape and sombrero shouting

"Adios Amoebas," could capture and hold the attention of otherwise sane, mature adults.

For anyone who can't appreciate a penguin wearing Fruit of the Loom jockey shorts while talking to a short, bespectacled intellectual named Ronald Ann, I feel pity. After all, in today's wacky world, what's so unusual about that?

Dan Graves

HOW'S THAT AGAIN?

Being a lifelong resident of the midwest eventually begins to leave telltale signs on a person that are easily recognizable to anyone from any other part of the country. For instance, residents of Aspen, Colorado, have to explain to a Hoosier why there are no John Deere dealers in town, and Floridians try to make us understand why it isn't necessary to call the Orkin man for sand crabs in the basement.

A Hoosier in Texas thinks armadillos are big rats with serious skin problems and that white wine doesn't go well with rattlesnake chili. Everyone thinks we can't pass up a hubcap lying along the road and our social standing is measured by the number of old cars we have up on blocks in the front yard.

Sure, we have a larger supply of mules, 1965 Ford Fairlanes, and porch swings than anywhere else in the world. At least we do know you can't plow with a Fairlane and we don't ride the mule to town on Saturday night, but what better place to watch a beautiful sunset and moonrise than from a creaky old porch swing?

I believe we got this reputation because they're jealous of our ability to raise tall corn and good looking women. We

80

also believe in an eye for an eye, a tooth for a tooth, and a quarter for a good cigar.

Some day I'll turn a beaver loose on the plains in Kansas and read the newspaper reports later of sightings of a huge buck-toothed prairie dog chewing down fence posts, or how the citizens of Flatbottom are forming a posse to hunt down what is believed to be a specimen of the formerly extinct platypus. In other words, other areas have their hang-ups too.

It's a tough job being a hillbilly. Trying to explain to someone from "New Yawk" what a groundhog is or describing how milk is really obtained to a citizen of Detroit can be frustrating. We can take a small measure of comfort in the fact that our neighbor across the Ohio river is in the same boat. We tell stories about Kentuckians and I'm sure their jokes about us are just as complimentary. Someday, it will get out of hand and war will be declared, resulting in the winner having to assume the responsibility of feeding ten million prisoners and their livestock.

Such a burden could be avoided if every Hoosier chipped in a dollar toward the purchase of Kentucky (see Louisiana Purchase) and joined forces with them in a stand against the rest of the country. We could call the new state Hootuck. Our flag would be emblazoned with the Gold Medal flour emblem flanked with likenesses of Colonel Sanders and John Cougar Mellenkamp.

We could safely make fun of Boston accents, good ol' boy southern drawls, and New York fashion designers. Old animosities would dissolve and instead of marrying second cousins, Hoosiers and Kentuckians would join to produce a race of demolition derby drivers and beer drinkers like the world has never seen. Certain cultural barriers will have to be overcome however, before such a union can take place.

With a purchase price already agreed on, scholars from both states will have to confer on a method of breaking down the language barrier that exists between the neighbors. Trips to foreign countries require weeks of studying books and tapes so that the traveler can ask some of the simpler questions, such as, "does this bus go all the way to Baghdad," or the ability to respond to those sidewalk vendors in exotic places with "no thank you, I don't want to meet your sister."

The following is a list of the more important pronunciations and definitions that should be known by both sides should such a union take place.

"ARN" – A heated device used to straighten wrinkles in clothing. A device used by golfers just prior to their releasing a string of profanity.

THANG" – An object. A statement normally preceded by "You sweet".

"STOWER" – A place where purchases are made, such as groceries or motor oil.

"LIKKER" – A liquor normally produced at remote places by use of old rusty buckets, car radiators, copper tubing and corn. Sometimes available at a stower.

"TAR" – Round, black rubber devices filled with air normally used to hold up automobiles.

"DOWER" – A device made of wood and hung on hinges at the entrance to dwellings and stowers.

"FLAR" – Attractive, blooming plants. An ingredient of bread and other baked goods.

"FAR" – To burn. An event that attracts large, red trucks and sightseers. The word used by Stonewall Jackson to his troops when the Redcoats finally opened their eyes and revealed the white parts.

"THANK" – To concentrate. Make decisions or create ideas. Common usage; "Don't bother me. I'm tryin' to thank."

"CRICK" – A small stream of water. Something one gets in their neck while watching a tennis match.

"CHAR" – An item of furniture commonly used for sitting and complaining about such things as rhumatiz and the dad-gummed government.

"DRANK" – To consume a liquid. Normally followed by "a big orange."

"PEEWADDIN" – Something to kick out of someone.

The above is a small example of some of the more common pronunciations used in everyday conversations. For those citizens of either state who either graduated from high school or are immigrants from other areas, I would recommend that you study the native language until you are capable of conversing intelligently. Imagine the confusion between a Californian and a resident of Hootuck on say, squirrel hunting.

Hootuck – "Wanna go squarl huntin', boy?"

Californian – "What's a squarl?"

Hootuck – "That's a critter kinda looks lak a long haired raet 'at lives in trees an' ets kowern. If ya keeps a light load in yer charcoal burner, ya won't be passin' too much shot after ya 'et 'em. Me, personal, I like to use a ball an' bark 'em by wangin' the limb they's settin' on. 'At way ya don't have ta worry 'bout lead poisonin.".

Californian – I understand that lead poisoning can affect a person's mental faculties. You eat a lot of squarl, don't you?"

Hootuck – "Yeh, an' maybe yore right, but I ain't livin' in no state what's got a big crack in it an' what's gonna fall

83

off into the ocean someday. If I was you, boy, I'd trade them roller blades fer water wangs."

Long live Hootuck.

YOU MEAN MEN AND WOMEN ARE DIFFERENT?

(Whoever came up with the notion that birds and bees had anything in common with sex was operating one bale short of a full loft. What does laying eggs and stinging have to do with sex?)

It finally dawned on me after year of marriage just how men and women differ (pause for the laughter to die down). I mean in personalities, life styles, priorities, and the way we approach everyday life in general. It comes as no surprise that men and women seem to be facing each other while paddling the canoe. Psychologists and counselors have covered this subject like fog on a pond for at least a thousand years. Cleopatra and old what's-his-name had trouble deciding who was going to deal, even in those days, and it hasn't got any better since. All of this struck me when I accompanied Judy to the grocery store.

Out of habit, I followed her into the store where she would make the selection of groceries for the coming week. I watched as she dropped cans and packages in the cart, none of which appealed to my taste buds. Since my services as a pack mule weren't immediately necessary, I began wandering the aisles and reading the ingredients on labels and mentally computing the daily intake required to prove fatal to the consumer.

It suddenly dawned on me, while staring at the cereal section that a husband is as out of place in a grocery store as a cat in the dog pound. I shop once in a while, but only for specific items, such as those rare times when I have to fend for myself. Then, it's a trip to the local doughnut shop for a nutritious pastry and a cup of coffee. When asked for my opinion on the fare for a meal, I normally answer, "I dunno," or, "a strawberry and sardine pot pie sounds good." In other words, I have no interest in food selection and simply eat whatever shows up on the table.

On the other hand, Judy will follow me through a gun and knife show or around the showroom of a motorcycle shop with the same blank look. The answers to my pleadings are entirely different, though. Why should I have to explain why a new rifle or the latest in two-wheeled technology is necessary for my continued good nature when she doesn't hear me complaining when she serves macaroni and cheese sandwiches with dirt pudding. Differing viewpoints and values.

The two of us shopping for clothes is like the rerun of an old Abbot and Costello movie. I'll follow her into a ladies clothing store like a retarded Basset Hound and spend what seems like a week leaning on racks, counting ceiling tiles and explaining to sales clerks that I'm not a cross dresser and the person they want to talk to is the lady with all the money in her purse. Why don't I wait outside or find something else to do? Because 99% of the shops in malls are women's clothing stores and it's too far to walk to Big

Bob's Motorcycle and Tattoo shop. Besides, I need to be present to make snide comments about women's fashions and how the clothing designers are apparently sniffing too much glue.

After talking myself out of a square meal for a week, we head for the men's clothing establishment. While my wife considers coordinated outfits, I'm about as fashion conscious as a junk yard dog. I consider the avoidance of public nakedness as the only reason for clothing purchases. As a result, I lean on racks, count ceiling tiles, and make snide comments on men's fashion designs while she decides whether I should look like the Marlboro Man or Elton John. Even prehistoric men were better decision makers than me. They dragged a mastadon home and said, "You cook meat, me wear skin." These days the wife drags home the meat and tells the man to put on the zoot suit she bought.

Driving a car is another area of differing opinions between men and women. My idea of the responsibility of the right seat passenger is to take whatever the driver wants to dish out. One day, while driving through an intersection, Judy screamed something that sounded like, "Look out for that Baltimore and Ohio freight train pulling a hundred cars going fifty miles an hour." After pulling my foot out of the firewall with the brake pedal welded to it, we had a discussion about the proper method of informing the driver of a potentially disastrous situation. Apparently, the lesson was learned, because later she remained silent until the dust settled after I pulled in front of another car at an intersection. Unfortunately, I was driving her car.

I, on the other hand, always remain calm with little comments like, "That's alright honey, that guy didn't need two rear view mirrors anyway." Actually, my normal seating position while she's driving is with both feet on the floor, shoulders against the seat back, my butt six inches off the seat, and my hands over my eyes. Okay, so my driving record is worse than hers. I can't help it if other people insist on being on the road at the same time as me.

I've had to explain to others that my passenger is not Michael Andretti; that it's just my wife in that full head cover crash helmet and Nomex fire proof racing suit. However, I am getting tired of her referring to herself as "Mrs. Tailspin Tommy."

In spite of differences, there are a few things we see eye to eye on. Our grandkids get away with things that would have drawn our kids two days in the stocks. We both agree that my ability to handle financial matters compares to Fidel Castro trying to dance in the Nutcracker Suite. I've made numerous attempts at keeping my checking account balance sheet at least within the same number of figures to the left of the decimal point as the bank, but so far, to no avail.

So what difference does a lousy fifty dollar deficit make? My motto is, you scratch my back and I'll scratch yours. If the bank will overlook an occasional overdraw, I'll not mention to anyone that those little Tootsie Rolls they keep at the tellers windows are so old, they crack your dentures if you attempt to chew them. Nevertheless, Judy insists on maintaining our finances and that's fine with me. The most important thing for married couples to remember is, don't fight over who's turn it is to put out the cat and bring in the dog, take turns changing the oil in the car, and never duck a left hook. By doing so, you set yourself up for a haymaker uppercut.

One final word of advice for the guys. Don't offer to serve her breakfast in bed and then bring in two slices of cold pizza and a beer. That menu may suit you just fine,

but you'll soon discover one more difference between the
sexes.

Dan Graves

BABY FORCES SALE OF CORVETTE

(The best ways to guarantee a sale on that old piece of junk in your garage is to tell the buyer you're either trying to finance a college education, pay for a hernia operation, or there's a baby on the way. Sure is funny how an unborn kid can be such an accomplished used car salesperson.)

One of life's greatest moments, when considering the responsibility that goes along with it, is the addition of children to the household. Since we have been blessed with two of our own and now a herd of grand kids, I feel highly qualified to give advice to other men on the proper methods of child rearing.

First and foremost, be sure your wife understands that you are very squeamish and you will not be present in the delivery room for the big moment. Simply inform her that you will make arrangements for a cameraman to videotape the whole thing and that you will watch the scene later. Apparently, the only thing missing from delivery rooms these days is a line of trumpeters to herald the arrival of the baby.

90

If it's a first child, most likely the only experience both parents will have with infants will have come from watching training films, or Bruce Willis in "Look Who's Talking".

As the time approaches, the mother wobbles around looking like she's trying to steal a medicine ball from the sporting goods department while struggling to maintain some semblance of fashion in her wardrobe. All efforts at everyday living are finally reduced to feeble attempts to get out of bed, go to the bathroom, eat breakfast, go to the bathroom, think about grocery shopping, go to the bathroom, attempt to train her husband to do the laundry and fix meals, go to the bathroom, stay in the bathroom, etc. Finally giving up on style, she wears t-shirts that say, "One In The Oven", or "Don't Blame Me. I Voted For Forced Vasectomy".

The husband, on the other hand, tries to be helpful by performing household chores, only to add to the misery by having to remove the cat's tail from the vacuum cleaner, put out nightly fires on the stove, or explain why he washed his bright red wool shirt with the formerly white linens.

Inevitably, by the eighth month he is blessed with inspiration and advertises his junk Corvette or motorcycle for sale, always ending the ad with "Must Sell. Baby On The Way". No one knows why an otherwise sane buying public is expected to fork over good cash for something that has been a neighborhood eyesore for years because "there's a baby on the way," but it seems to work better than "I'm tired of mowing around it."

Due to today's medical technology, the sex of the child will have been determined by the sixth month, thus relieving the parents of the guessing game of what color to paint the former laundry room, where they will begin spending most of their nights for the next year or two. A crib and solar powered musical mobile along with a ton of other baby related items soon fill the room from floor to ceiling.

The big day finally arrives and the heir to the family fortune makes his or her debut into the world. The proud father passes out cigars that smell like a fire in a compost heap and begins assaulting his friends and co-workers with pictures of his handy-work. The mother begins the task of getting herself back into shape while learning to exist on three hours of sleep every two days. She lugs forty pounds of baby luggage around while her husband proudly carries the seven pound bundle of joy. That is, until the passenger decides to relieve itself, at which time a role reversal occurs.

Thereafter, the family settles into the normal routine of an everyday life of changing diapers, overheating, cooling, then re-heating the formula and trying to outwit the baby and each other at the 2:00 a.m. feeding by pretend snoring as the former laundry room erupts in siren-like howls.

There are a few do's and don'ts that all first time parents should know if they are to raise a secure, happy child. If it's a boy, don't give him a football during the first year. Nothing destroys a child's confidence in its parents as fast as having them present him with something that looks and tastes like it came from the south end of an elephant. Besides, it must be terrifying to have a large, brown, oblong object sitting on your chest as your father makes funny noises and tries to get you to wrap your arms around it.

Everyone knows the first year with a baby can be very hectic - that every-day life demands our fullest attention. Don't get into such a hurry at the mall that you forget to take the baby out of the cart before leaving. It's tough enough to find a parking place that doesn't have a cart in it without the complication of having to deliver a baby to the lost and found department.

If you happen to be absent-minded, attach your home address and telephone number to the child before taking it anywhere. This will prevent a lot of trouble and will give the child a greater sense of security, especially after it has spent some time in the lost and found department. Don't worry.

Within two weeks you'll get used to having the child around and will miss it within a short time if it isn't there.

By all means, if you can gain fifteen seconds of friends and relatives time, show them pictures of your pride and joy. However, don't ask them their opinion on who the baby looks like. This is like asking them to compare a Mack Truck to a Volkswagen and inevitably they will, out of courtesy, say it looks just like whichever of the parents happen to be holding the picture. All babies look alike for a few months after birth (with the exception of Groucho Marx, who was born with a moustache).

Plan your activities carefully. A simple trip to the grocery can be a nightmare of logistics, with both parents working feverishly to load the diaper bag with all the necessities, fold the stroller and load it into the trunk, bundling the baby so well that it could stand a full blown Arctic blizzard and securing the car seat tight enough to withstand a space launch.

Half exhausted, you arrive at the destination only to reverse the above and then do it all over again before starting home. To make the trip at least seem worthwhile, drive at least a hundred miles for a loaf of bread or a gallon of milk.

There is one chore that men do not perform well, and that is changing diapers. Fortunately, nowadays, pins aren't necessary as new upholstery can be applied by simply wrapping it around the child and sticking it on with something that acts like Velcro. This saves a lot of embarrassment for the father and a lot of pain for the kid. After all, with today's laws concerning child abuse, it wouldn't do to have to answer questions as to why the kid looks like a dope addict, what with all the puncture marks on its bottom.

After the child is raised and on its own, it's time to start scouring the classified ads to replace that old Corvette you sold years ago. Look for the ads that end with "Have to sell. Baby on the way."

MULE TRADING, AUCTION BARNS, AND YARD SALES

(Everyone has a different opinion of what's valuable. If you buy an elephant for five dollars but can't sell it for six or eat it, maybe it isn't such a bargain after all.)

Those of us who are fortunate enough to live in the Midwest don't have much to do. There are no mountains to climb, no beaches to frolic on or vast forests or sky-blue lakes to soothe our souls. In the spring we plow the fields and plant corn. During the summer we sit on the back porch and watch it grow. Fall comes around and we harvest the crop. During the winter months we sit in front of a window and hope a car goes by to break the monotony.

We drive pick-up trucks with bumper stickers that say "This Is Not An Abandoned Vehicle", and for most of us, a Saturday night's entertainment is watching demonstration films on the overhead t.v. sets at Wal-Mart.

In spite of a lifestyle that – by comparison to, say, living in Colorado, is like working on a night crawler farm, we have forms of entertainment that sets us apart from the jet set crowd. Let the rest of them have their seasonal playgrounds, their bikini's and sports cars. We have Horse Trading, Auction Barns, and Yard Sales.

Horse trading originated, just as the name implies, when two people, each with what was once a horse, decided to follow the golden rule of "Do unto others before they do unto you." Each barterer runs the other's horse down as being about as valuable as a stack of broken bricks, while trying to get something else thrown into the trade.

The rules are simple. Find a courthouse lawn bench on a warm Saturday afternoon, sit and watch traffic for a while and then ease into the bargaining with as much finesse as possible. The normal session goes like this:

"That ol' nag of yores still eatin' you out of house and home?"

"You talkin' 'bout my lead plow horse or my mother-in-law?"

"I'm talkin' 'bout that thing that looks like a four-legged display of cheap carpet samples with a worn-out mop leanin' agin it."

"Don't look no worse than that thing you got. You ever consider puttin' a two-by-four down its back an' usin' ropes to pull its belly up to keep it from draggin' the ground?"

"Tell you what I'll do. I'll trade that fine animal of mine for yours if you'll throw in that rusty ol' shotgun the mice are usin' for a summer home."

"I'll just bet you would. That horse of mine has thoroughbred blood and that shotgun is a fine, old English fowling piece. I'll trade my horse for yours and that mangy thing you call a coon dog."

"Thoroughbred blood? More like thoroughdead, and yore right about that shotgun being a fouling piece. Fouls up every time you shoot it."

And so it continues until someone gets skinned, but finer entertainment can't be found outside a Tennessee mule auction. Which brings us to the second form of entertainment, which is near and dear to the hearts of mid-westerners, the Saturday night auction sale.

To some, an auction is like a black hole is space. If you get too close to it, you're sucked in like a snake into a vacuum cleaner. The scene is always the same. You roam around looking at all that fine merchandise, hoping to find the diamond in a lump of cheap coal. Finally, there it is, that one of a kind chrome plated, left-handed bottle opener you've been searching for since it became a priceless item to bottle opener collectors. Taking a seat, you vow to sell your grandmother into slavery rather than let someone else walk out with that gem.

Assuming your best "I don't give a hoot about anything here" look, you wait for the chosen item to be put on the block, at which time you'll subtly signal your bid by a slight nod of the head or a wiggle of a finger. After all, you've seen how the pro's do it by watching auctions at Sotheby's on t.v.

Just as they start the bidding on a bucket of nails and various other things that have been sitting behind the barn for years, and is rusted into what looks like a battered cannon ball, the only fly in the whole place decides to use your nose as a landing strip for the rest of the night.

Fear of flicking it off and signaling a false bid causes you to keep your hands down and you watch cross-eyed as the tiny bugger begins strolling around between your eyes, its scratchy little feet touching every nerve ending on your proboscis. It refuses to be blown off and seems to be enjoying the ride as you wriggle your nose as subtly as possible. Finally, unable to stand it any longer, you slowly lower your head, hoping to trap the tiny demon between your knees where you will proceed to slowly pull off its wings while listening to its shrill little screams of pain. While you dream of other, more exquisite forms of fly torture, the auctioneer throws the left-handed bottle opener into the nail keg as bait for further bidding and an Amish farmer becomes the proud owner of your obsession.

You finally buy an axe handle, even though you don't have an axe head, and go home swearing never again to visit one of these dens of inequity. Until next week, that is.

Last but not least is that paragon of American ingenuity and free enterprise, the yard sale. Someone, no doubt to their surprise, found a profitable way to transfer all their worthless junk from the basement and garage by capitalizing on the old phrase, "one man's junk, another man's treasure". The word spread faster than fleas in a dog pound. As a result, my wife and I, during the summer months, engage in constantly revolving mobile inventory shopping.

The way I see it, the stuff we buy this week will be sold at our sale next week. It will then re-appear in another sale within a year, thus keeping the same junk on the road forever. I could swear that I've seen an old orange juice squeezer with a chipped edge five times over the past two years at sales in three counties. These outdoor variety stores attract crowds faster than a dinner bell on a hog farm. Out of bed at 5:00 a.m. on Saturday and armed with the classified ads, glassy-eyed shoppers take to the roads in search if life's most elusive quarry. A bargain.

Tables sit in driveways filled with everything from worn-out mousetraps, to six-foot sections of chain link fence and fragged-out tennis shoes. Books, ten for a dollar, racks of fifties style clothing, Ball jars and puzzles with only five pieces missing give rise to, "What the heck. It's fun, isn't it?"

Loaded with priceless junk, you can't wait to put it all back out in your sale where you'll sell it for ten cents less than you gave for it. After all, what other forms of entertainment do we have in the mid-west?

I'll bet people from California think a yard sale means we strip the sod off our lawn and peddle it. If you're from Los Angeles and are reading this, that's not true. If we did that, the goats wouldn't have anywhere to graze.

PIZZA, CANDY, YES – SAGGING UNDERWEAR, NO

(Trying to reason with a 2-year old is like talking to a dog. At least the dog pretends it knows what you're talking about.)

I've finally learned the difference between parents and grandparents. One is a full time job for life with no retirement plan, but full benefits, and the other is part-time, but with the same benefits. However, with the part-time job you can circumvent parental authority without a guilty conscious. Parents say "No, and if you do it anyway you'll be rattling chains in the attic until you're 21." Grandparents say, "Sure, go ahead, but don't tell your parents."

Okay, so most grandparents have an attitude. Go ahead, sue us. We worked hard to get the title and we're not about to let anyone usurp our authority when it comes to such simple things as dropping the occasional rock in the parental churn.

Our parents did it to us when we were trying to impress on our children that not everything in life is free or readily available for the asking. Turnabout is fair play.

Now our children can listen to those infamous words from their kids that echo from a time when they used them. "But, grandma and grandpa said we could."

One weekend I had the opportunity to exercise my power as the grandparent when I was given the job of entertaining two of my grandsons for a few hours on Saturday afternoon. Making them stand at attention, I paced back and forth in front of them and outlined the rules for the day.

Rule number 1: No fighting over the type of topping on the pizza.

Rule number 2: No more than two hours in each toy department and no "His toy cost more than mine."

Rule number 3: Electronic games could be played only after all candy and ice cream had been consumed, thus preventing my having to pry sticky fingers off the keyboards.

Finally, rule number 4 was the biggie: The first guy to use his shorts as a potty would be required to recite the entire Preamble to the Constitution and then walk home.

I explained that I had never been one to willingly re-upholster my own children when accidents happened and I was not about to change my ways in my old age. When I was sure they understood the rules, I slid the cattle prod under my belt, slung the bull whip over my shoulder, removed their handcuffs and loaded them in the vehicle for an afternoon of male bonding.

The first sign of insurrection came when I asked them if they would like to roam through a few used car lots and then drive to the airport and watch airplanes take off and land. I might as well have suggested that we window shop at a health food store. When the votes were finally tallied, we stopped at their favorite pizza parlor for a fine repast of glom covered round crust and Mountain Dew.

This particular establishment had small TV sets in each booth and a cute little electric train that delivered the drink orders. For a quarter, the kids could play a video game on the TV where a hedgehog (or some such critter) skitters through obstacles collecting gold rings while avoiding hedgehog eating carnivores and pits full of long, sharp spikes.

After the little Baltimore and Ohio delivered the drinks and the pizza was ordered, I dropped a quarter in the thing and watched as Matt, the oldest, engaged in the hedgehog wars while David, the 2-year old, transfixed by the cliff-hanging action, sat like a stone and watched as the electronic drama unfolded. Then came a pizza that was slightly black around the edges and covered with enough grease to lubricate the transmission of a bulldozer. With kids however, a pizza could be made of shredded tires with a plywood crust and they would whine only if they thought they weren't getting their share.

The table was soon covered with pizza crud; David looked like he had used the no-hands method of dining, and I was headed for a classic case of indigestion. Finished with the magnificent repast, we leaned back, fired up cigars, and engaged in casual conversation. When I asked their opinion of the Bosnian conflict, Matt reflected for a moment as though preparing to offer a profound solution to the problem, then asked for another quarter to continue the hedgehog wars. David then looked at me and casually declared, "I don't have to go potty."

A shiver coursed through me at these words. I knew how Mussolini would have felt if someone had told him during his trial, "Don't worry, you'll probably get off on a misdemeanor charge." Like a prosecutor grilling a witness, I asked, "Do you have to go potty?"

"Huh-uh, I don't have to go potty."

"Have you already gone potty?"

"Huh-uh, I don't have to go potty."

How do you get across to a 2-year old that he isn't going to be forced to go potty, but that confession is good for the soul and that he might as well be in the middle of the Sahara Desert as far as replacement underwear is concerned. At this point I began subtly sniffing the air around the table to see if the defendant was lying. No evidence was immediately apparent, so I figured that until people started giving us a wide berth, it was safe to remain in public. At least until he was found guilty.

Next came the toy department of a large variety store and a resurgence of memories of times with my own kids. With aisle after aisle of plastic and rubber goodies to bounce, push, and squeeze, Matt flitted about like a butterfly in a daisy patch. One could follow his progress by the electronic noise as he ran along pushing buttons on noise toys.

David was more reserved as he paused to admire individual wonders, giving each a thorough scrutiny before moving on to the next. After an hour of "Can I have this?", and "Why not?", I felt like Ma Kettle after she found out she was expecting another one.

There followed a period of negotiations in which decisions were made on the choice of toys and pricing, then it was home and an evening of dodging foam rubber darts and waiting for the women to return from a shopping trip so David could be re-upholstered and allowed back into the house.

I can't say it was any more frustrating the second time around (after experiencing the same trips with my own brood), but it sure was better than any other way I could think of to spend a Saturday afternoon.

SPECIAL FOODS FOR NOCTURNAL CINEMAS

The sound of the powerful engine in the blood red Ferrari rose and fell, echoing off the hills on both sides of the twisting road as the machine responded to the skilled hands and swift reflexes of its driver. Like a howling crimson demon, the crescendo of the engine wavering in the still night air, it sped toward the palace with headlights illuminating the parade of huge billboards advertising Fredericks of Hollywood and Victoria's Secret. Pulling to a stop at the curb, I removed my kid leather driving gloves while gazing at the magnificent structure that was the home of the king of this insignificant little country.

As the valet approached my car, I reached into a brown paper bag sitting on the seat beside me and grabbed a handful of one hundred dollar bills as a tip, wondering why the king had summoned me, especially on such short notice. My attire of nothing but purple cowboy boots and unlit cigar seemed inappropriate for the occasion, but urgency had left little time for clothing.

Acutely aware of my lack of attire, I climbed from the car, rushed for the huge door, tripped on the curb and fell out of bed. Such a rude awakening left me with three emotions: relief, regret, and remorse.

Relief at not having to stand in front of the king dressed only in a smile, regret that I hadn't brought the money sack and Ferrari with me, and remorse over wearing the purple cowboy boots. I always looked better in the green and yellow pair.

Such are the things that dreams are made of. I used to think sleeping was a waste of time; a time when the world passed me by as I lay in a comatose state of unawareness while dust mites chewed on my toes. I've since discovered that with my lifetime pass to the Subconscious Ritz, I can experience all the pleasure of being pursued by terrifying, slavering monsters while wading through hip deep molasses, or trip lightly through fields of flowers at the Rosy Cheek Nudist Colony, and live the breathtaking freedom of soaring above the world in serene, powerless flight.

If dreams are, as the experts say, the subconscious mind expressing the fears, hopes, and fantasies that each of us have, then mine must be wearing a zoot suit while roller skating through Toon Town. I wouldn't wish a cross-eyed, duck-walking, drum pounding, Elmer Fudd type subconscious like mine on anyone. This thing must spend all its time sitting with its feet dangling over a piranha pit "dreaming" up the program each night, giggling and whooping when it comes up with an especially good piece of entertainment.

Sometimes it causes things to become physical, as my wife discovered one night. I was in the midst of a particularly sticky situation involving myself and a group of belligerent well-armed mercenaries, when a rattlesnake with a mouth big enough to swallow a Volkswagen appeared. Afterward, I thought the addition of the snake was a little tacky but dismissed it as a harmless prank by the id. Terrified, I swung at the critter and bellowed out a yell that shook windows for a block. Unfortunately, she happened to be lying about where the snake was and received the full force of the blow. I spent the next hour trying to coax her into putting down the baseball bat and returning to bed.

Even though I explained the reason for the attack, she kept the bat leaning against the headboard for the rest of the night and fell asleep muttering something about one good turn deserving another.

The activity of the subconscious during sleep still puzzles the scientific community. The reasons for the subject of dreams has been as elusive as a gossamer butterfly that flutters just out of reach, denying us the doorway to the inner self. I, however, in a series of experiments, have discovered the key that unlocks the door to the office of the nocturnal program manager's office.

Food!

We can control the subject material of our nightly entertainment (if you wish to call it that) by what we eat before retiring. Exhaustive research and countless tons of antacids and laxatives have resulted in my being able to select the program in which I wish to participate. The following fare just before bedtime is guaranteed to get the desired results:

Wolfman Meets Me: Prepare a pound of ground beef (extra lean) by opening the package and dropping it into a cereal bowl. Sprinkle liberally with extra hot Tabasco sauce and marinate with a quart of black strap molasses. Stuff it down as fast as possible with a minimum of chewing. Go to bed and fall asleep whispering "I'm not afraid of wolves; Lon Chaney was just an actor."

I guarantee that by midnight you'll be climbing the headboard while kicking your pillow into a blizzard of feathers.

Romancing The (Sharon) Stone: Using a large mixing bowl, blend one quart dill pickles, a pint of whipping cream, two blended hot dogs, a tablespoon of black pepper, and a package of instant vanilla pudding. Bake for five hours at 400 degrees and serve warm while reading a couple of chapters of Red Hot Mama.

Be prepared to be awakened in the middle of the night by your wife slapping your face and screaming, "Who is she, you no-good rat?"

This recipe is recommended only for singles or those who like to live or sleep dangerously. The above works equally well for ladies with the exception of the reading material. A good selection is The Life and Times of Hugh Grant With Pictures.

Superman Special: Bake a large turkey in the usual manner, dip a drumstick in chocolate, sprinkle with ground, hot jalapeno pepper and serve with a slice of angel food cake. Soon after falling asleep, you'll be soaring among the clouds with no visible means of support, the world spreading out below you like a magnificent tapestry.

Unfortunately, this tapestry sometimes ends up looking just like the bedroom carpet, but if the pile is deep enough and the bed sits close to the floor, the fall won't hurt you.

Enjoy your dreams while remembering that they are a release of those innermost desires or fears that we as mortal beings can only hope will come true or stay hidden. If you awake some morning only to find you're chained to the wall in a dank, dark dungeon, then maybe a baseball bat by the bedside isn't so bad after all.

ROLE REVERSALS FOR TODAY'S POLITICIANS

(Not much good can be said about politicians. One thing's for sure, though. Most of them shovel their manure out of different barns.)

I've been told that some things such as religion, politics, and eggs that have been left in the barn too long are best left alone unless one wishes to stir up a real stink.

Since I'm already walking on thin ice with the man upstairs, and having been on the receiving end of my share of barn eggs, there's only one trap left to put my foot in. To make this real interesting, what I know about politics wouldn't fill the saddle on a flu germ, but it seems that those who know the least say the most and get the lion's share of the attention.

Historically, politics has proven to be a profession that is, at one end, lackadaisical ("without vigor or determination", according to Webster) and at the other end, downright dangerous. Politicians have been speared, hung, whipped, shot, tarred-and-feathered, and run out of town on a rail. Most of the ones who got into trouble forgot their opinion doesn't count for more than one vote. They failed to listen to the majority of their constituents. It should be painfully clear by now that the fastest way to get your hair parted by a Yankee musket ball is to get elected to office and then try to do things your way.

When election years roll around I wonder how politicians of long ago conducted their campaigns. I suspect that the normal reaction from most voters in the first presidential election was "George who?" The candidates didn't have the advantage of radio, television, telephone poles to decorate with posters, or billboards to assault the citizenry.

How many of today's office seekers would consider riding a mule 30 miles to stand in front of a tobacco chewing crowd and try to convince them that if elected he would rid the town of everything from barn rats to bad whiskey. Like today, voters then probably figured that the barn rats would eventually outsmart the politician, and there is no such thing as bad whiskey.

Wouldn't it be interesting if some of today's more prominent politicians were to be transported back in time and placed in the shoes of past historical figures? It could go something like this:

The year is 1816 and the great leader has returned to France after being defeated at Waterloo. Standing before an angry king of France is Napoleon NIXON.

King: "Explain yourself varlot. You who were the conqueror of half the civilized world and the leader of the movement to stabilize our foreign markets in Louie The Third antiques have allowed yourself to be soundly defeated by a rabble rousing horde of Belgiamites. Also, word has reached me through news hawks that you were involved in scandalous means of attaining harmful information on your second-in-command, General Francois Lepew. Speak quickly in your defense or face imprisonment."

Napoleon: "Well, just let me say this about that. It wasn't my fault. I have been unjustly accused of undermining the enemy by stealing their children and giving my subordinates the command to sneak behind enemy lines and heist their "Brussels" sprouts, thus facilitating the capture of all my troops and losing the battle. And, as for General Lepew, well, I'm not a sneak. I don't need to muckrake that slug to prove his incompetence. He's going to stick his own neck in the noose."

The scene shifts to 1789 in America and an interview of that young country's soon to be first president, George CARTER:

"Mr. Carter, Hezekiah Jones of the Washington Lampoon here. What is your view on the nullification of the British?"

George: "Ah figga' tha'et they been nullified enough. Ah personally wouldn't want to show ma' face in public aftah bein' whipped by a bunch'a hog fahma's (grin)."

Hezekiah: "You have quite an accent. Are you from the south?"

George: "No suh. Ah'm from around he'a. It's these teeth. Ah asked for 'em to be made from red oak but some fool cawved 'em from white pine. A'hm gittin' splinters in ma lips."

The year is 1861 and preparations are underway for a speech by the new president, Abraham REAGAN:

Abraham: "Four score and eleven years ago, our forefathers brought forth on this continent——."

"Cut, cut, cut! Aby baby, it's seven years, not eleven. Will someone PLEASE turn up the gaslights so he can see the script. Look Abe, I've been meaning to talk to you about that outfit. Maybe we should try to boost your image with something other than basic black. Let's replace that stovepipe with, say, a Stetson. That'll give you better reviews in the south. While you're at it, could you ask Nancy not to go through that little song and dance routine while you're on stage?"

"MAKEUP!"

"See if you can do something about that wart. It stands out like boots on a mule. Ready to try it again, Abe?"

Abe: "Well, I—ah, hmmm, ah—, what was the question again?"

The year is 1865 and the two military leaders of a war weary country face each other across the table at Appomattox. They are Ulysses S. Grant and Robert E. CLINTON.

Ulysses: "Sir, your armies are depleted and your supplies exhausted, and you are being soundly defeated on every front. I respectfully request you accept our terms of surrender."

Robert: "Ah can see that these are very good terms suh, but ah have a better plan. We'll both surrender. Working together as a team, we can build a strong government with a bright future for us as a united America. You'all can continue to smoke your cigars and I can jog in safety and confidence on streets free of crime and poverty. So, if you agree suh, just lay down your guns first, and then we'll do the same."

Ah, the good old days of winning public office by saddle sores, standing on a genuine soap box, and painted slogans on barns seem to be gone. Ours is still the best system in the world, but even the finest of machines occasionally needs a little repair. As the sheriff of a small town said as he questioned the chief suspect who denied the charges of horse stealing:

"Son, I ain't nearly as interested in finding out how you got into the barn as I am in finding out how you managed to talk all them horses into following you home."

Keep that in mind the next time Senator Fogbottom waves his hands and shouts out that he promises to right all the evils in the world.

A BIRDS-EYE VIEW OF THE WORLD

(The older we get, the harder it seems to be to keep up with the crowd. Maybe we should pull over to the curb and direct traffic instead.)

While performing a few minor repairs on the house one day, I decided to climb on up to the roof, wrap my toes over the edge and see why the pigeons, who seem to spend the bigger part of their day doing just that, are so fascinated with such a waste of time. Three of them kindly moved over to give me room, and within a short while, I was cooing and bobbing my head in unison with them.

The house faces a busy intersection and it was obvious that the local exhaust systems repair shops were doing a lousy business. Half the vehicles that passed sounded like they were built under government contract, while the tire dealers were rolling in luxury. Enough rubber was being burned into the pavement to make the neighborhood smell like a fire in the city dump.

I asked myself, what kind of recreation do pigeons get out of bellowing exhaust pipes and squealing tires. I know these birds aren't noted for their love of hanging around on the back stretch of the Brickyard 400, and since their only occupation seems to be messing up the sidewalk in front of the house and making more pigeons, there had to be some other reason for such casual entertainment.

It finally dawned on me. Since pigeons never seem to be in a hurry to do anything, they were sitting there watching the human population scurry around like rats from a barn fire. From our vantage point (the other pigeons and I), the scene below looked like a scene from the Keystone Kops as cars ripped in every direction and joggers flashed by in their quest for healthier cardiovascular systems. I knew that in other parts of town and the rest of the world schedules were being met with the aid of faster and faster computers, hoardes of travelers were whistling along in sleek jets and fast food joint were shoveling greasy quick burgers into customers by the ton.

As we watched the mayhem, I wondered what the outcome would have been if some of our more prominent figures from the past had been caught up in our present day "get it done yesterday" environment.

The first one that came to mind was Michelangelo as he painted the ceiling of the Sistine Chapel. A priest yells up at him as he works:

"Hey, Mike. Nice work, but the Pope has asked if you can step it up a bit. He's expecting a budget committee from the central office here next week and they'll be looking to see how much bang they're getting for their buck. So, he wants to see the ceiling done by then. Oh, yeah, one more thing. The bishop says that if you're going to work during services, could you cool it on the singing. He's having a hard time on his delivery while you're belting out "Ninety-Nine Bottles of Beer On The Wall."

A week later the committee stands gazing at the finished ceiling.

"What in the name of all the saints does that represent?"

"Mike says it's a 100 mile per hour collage of all the significant events in the history of Christianity."

"It looks more like a major explosion in a paint factory."

During the early forties a significant event is taking place at the University of Chicago. On a squash court under the west stands of Stagg Field, scientists are constructing the world's first atomic pile, hoping to attain a sustained chain reaction, which will lead to development of the atomic bomb. There, Fermi, Anderson and others work, carefully stacking blocks of graphite to the precise size in order to sustain the neutron loss from the uranium in the lattice. Enter a (what else) government representative sent to evaluate the progress being made.

"Looks good, fellas. How much longer until we can expect results?"

"How long? No can wait. Here, I'll help you stack these things and then we'll throw the switch."

"Whaddaya mean, we could all be exposed to radiation and turn into toads with green warts on our noses if we don't follow the plan? Don't worry about it. Uncle Sam will take care of everything, so let's get cracking. What's radiation, anyway?"

The next day's headlines read:

"Squash Court Squashed."

"Stagg Scientists Stumped."

"Mysterious Green Glow Settles Over University Stadium."

"According to Scientists, Haste Makes Waste."

The old saying of "There's never time to do it right, but plenty of time to do it over" has never been more true than it is today. Fortunately, nature has a way of balancing things. As we get older, we begin to develop resistance to life in the fast lane. What was "do or die" yesterday becomes a "do it and die" situation today. During our youth we fight to stay, if not in front of the herd, at least in it, moving at the same speed. However, as the years pass, the herd gets more and more in a state of stampede and then you're spending time trying to avoid getting run over or stepping in something.

Finally, you begin to slow down and do a little grazing. What was all important to get done immediately yesterday, seems to take on a degree of insignificance as you greet each day with the feeling of satisfaction of finally taking the time to "do it right" the first time. Of course, there are times when the rest of the herd may look at you and say, "Get out of the way, you old—— (fill in the blank as you see fit), or, "if you wish to remain competitive, you must upgrade to the latest 200 gigabyte, super hetrodyne, monocular transducer processor."

Since joining my newest feathered friends, I've found that they could care less about anything but a warm chimney to sit on in the winter months and a two-story house that affords them a clear view of the hustle and bustle of the world below. All they need is a well stocked corn crib, an ample supply of weeds with which to build a nest, and a neighborhood free of B-B guns.

If you'll excuse me, the boys and I are going to fly downtown, find a few window ledges to mess up and watch the world scratch and claw itself through another day.

ALPHONSO T. FOGBOTTOM FOR PRESIDENT

After every election, local or national, we can begin practicing our "Why did I vote for that @#$%^# no-good scoundrel" while settling down for another few years of feeling like they (whoever "they" are) have our faces on voodoo dolls. "They" will spend their entire term poking these dolls with pins and cackling maniacally as we jerk and squirm in agony. Some of us try to avoid any involvement in the mess by pasting on bumper stickers that read, "Don't Blame Me. I Voted For——."

It's amazing how much political campaigning is like fishing with a night crawler dressed in a clown suit and hanging from a rusty hook. The suckers (voters) cautiously nose the ridiculous bait as it smiles and dances on the hook. Even as the sucker wonders how it's going to digest the clown suit, it opens wide and swallows.

Not me. I turn the tables on those witch doctors when I vote. Armed with a punch card and a pin, I enter the little booth with all the candidates' names in what looks like a flip page book. "Nyuck, Nyuck" I laugh as I slide the card in place and begin poking the pin into the hole beside the candidate that I wouldn't wish on the warden of the worst prison in Siberia. Sometimes I poke the same hole more than once while chanting "Oom Na Mana Padma Oom" over and over.

It's a great feeling knowing that for once, they are dancing to my tune. Then, as the election returns roll in, I can see where I had been effective in some areas but had missed the mark in others. I finally have to admit that some politicians, being pretty greasy characters, manage to slip through and get elected anyway. Mulling over my choices of who to poke and who not to, I thought back on the TV and radio campaign ads and their effect on my decisions.

Some of them left me with the impression that the candidates spend a lot of time stealing their opponents garbage cans and sifting through them, while the rest of the time they work to keep their own cans from being exposed. If half the charges being thrown around were true, we'd be voting to parole our favorite candidates so they would be able to work out of an office instead of a prison cell. Maybe the day will come when campaign posters will be mug shots and we'll vote for their prisoner I.D. number.

A typical ad normally goes like this: A still picture of the opposing candidate, his hair disheveled and every wart on his face highlighted, flashes on the screen for shock effect. As a voice that sounds like an executioner reading the provisions of the proceedings drones in the background, statistics on the evil deeds performed by this devil scroll across the screen.

"Who voted NO to the repeal of Joan of Ark's sentence and who voted YES to raise taxes 100% to pay for five hundred more Congressional swimming pools while he was committing a class A felony by having 10 veterans of

WW1 put to death for singing "The Old A.T.F Just Ain't What He Used To Be?" Alphonso T. Fogbottom, that's who. Would you want this man to continue representing you in Congress?"

"Vote for honesty, integrity, and faith in the American dream. Vote for Alphonso T. Fogbottom Junior and let him prove that a Fogbottom tradition for the past forty years can change. Remember, "If it isn't a Fogbottom deal (at this point he tears up what looks suspiciously like a summons), then you really don't have a deal."

By the time the commercial ends, you're thoroughly convinced that an attendant has left the back door of the asylum unlocked and most of the inmates somehow ended up in Washington.

I don't pretend to understand the logic behind such advertisements, but why does a candidate spend $50,000 a minute to mention his opponents name thirty times and his own only once? For that kind of money, I'd forget about muckraking and take sixty seconds to convince the audience that I'm an alien and if they don't vote for me, I'll turn the whole planet into a giant prune. Better yet, why not take the same amount of money, head for the nearest sports car dealership and tack up a few posters on telephone poles along the way. The surest way to get me to vote to rid the world of evil, truth-less politicians is to have one stand with his hand on a copy of "American Justice The Hard Way" and proclaim his innocence to the charges by his opponents that he purchased his private island in the Bahamas with money he earned selling used cars, part time.

When election day finally comes, my wife and I sit watching the returns, alternating between deep despair and exuberant shouts of "YES—TAKE THAT YOU SLANDEROUS SALAMANDER. THAT'LL TEACH

YOU TO MESS WITH THE COALITION FOR A SIN FREE SOCIETY!"

Then, one day my wife dropped a bombshell on me. Watching a score sheet on the screen I asked, "What's this Electoral College and what's their curriculum and why are they advertising it on the election returns? I thought Budweiser would be more likely to be able to afford that kind of ad space."

"No dear, you don't understand," she said. "Each state has one and its number is decided by the size of the voting population. The Electoral College casts its votes to determine who will be the president."

I was stunned.

With a quivering voice I asked, "You mean that after all that pin poking and high hopes and wearing the little sticker that says "I Voted" (I felt so ashamed), people who probably don't have a degree, from a college that doesn't have a campus or a football team, will actually elect the president?"

"That's the way it works," she said.

"How do I know if my college person voted the way I did?"

"They are required to vote according to the popular vote unless it turns out to be a 50-50 tally. Then they cast their ballot according to their own wishes."

I have now come to the conclusion that everyone in the country should apply for admission to that college and take courses in the political and agricultural sciences, especially bean farming.

When we can understand what motivates politicians to pursue their chosen career and why so much gas is generated in Washington, maybe we as voters can grasp the big fuss over the degeneration of our ozone layer. Somehow, I get the feeling there's a connection. Better yet, enclose that entire city in an air tight and escape-proof dome and let the rest of us breathe easier.

MONEY – THE ROOT AND BRANCHES OF ALL EVIL

(You can always tell the rich man from the poor. The rich man has a two-hole outhouse with a partition between the stalls.)

It's quite apparent that some things in life hold more importance than others. For instance, you see more people breathing than, say, taking ballet lessons. That seems like a poor analogy, but we place unreasonable emphasis on trivial things, while the possibility of California breaking off the continent and floating off into the Pacific Ocean causes no more concern than dents in a garbage can.

Take baseball for instance. Here is a sport where a bunch of guys stand around on a field watching one of their guys throw a ball at another guy, who having just come out of a hole in the ground called a dugout, tries to hit the ball with a round club and who, if he gets lucky and hits it, runs like hell for what is called first base. The other guys who are standing on the field try to get the ball and bean the runner with it. Then, the guys on the field (who each receive $10,000,000 a year) resume their position of looking bored and kicking at the astro-turf until the next guy crawls out of the hole with a round stick in his hand.

The only thing that wouldn't cause a die-hard baseball fan to scream bloody murder if the televised game were interrupted with an important bulletin would be news that an asteroid had struck and destroyed the Budweiser brewery.

The one subject, however, that the mere mention of will attract an audience faster than a hog singing The Jailhouse Rock is money. Money and how to get more of it seems to be the driving force behind our very existence. No one is immune to the effect money has on our lives.

I know a man who's so tight he wouldn't pay a nickel to watch a garter snake swallow a football. However, he would then bet the same nickel that the snake would survive a fifty yard field goal attempt. Money can be made or lost in an infinite variety of ways, but the most common are honest labor, begging, stealing, discreet use of a printing press, or financial investments. Perhaps a review of each would be in order.

Honest Labor: YUK! I know this is the method most commonly used for financial gain, but consider the drawbacks inherent with the use of moneys earned by this method. Hard work seems to addle the mind and cause unwise decisions when it comes to making purchases. The first thing most people do is buy a new car. Let's assume you purchased one for $20,000 and have taken the usual six year loan at 12% interest compounded daily with a balloon clause that is subject to variations on the world petroleum market, pro-rated hourly.

Using the above variables it's easy to see that, figuring interest on borrowed capital (however that's figured), cost of licensing and excise taxes, depreciation, insurance, daily fluctuations in the cost of fuel, and the annual cost of an extended warranty, your outlay for the first year will be $21, 964.47. The balance at the end of the first year will then be $19,963.74. Total outlay after six years - $234,462.89. Value of the car at payoff – Bucks Automobile Cemetery. That is, if you call Buck and make arrangements to pay $75 for him to come haul it away. Most new car purchasers could feed the entire island of Saipan for a year on their personal transportation costs. But, what the heck! What else could the money be used for?

Begging: This method requires only two things: a talented monkey and a pair of dark glasses. I've found that Rhesus monkeys seem to be more profitable than spider monkeys, probably because of their ability to charm a crowd. They're also better at deciding how the money should be spent.

If prying monkeys off your arm isn't your forte, try the direct approach by getting on your knees and grabbing passersby by the leg and let them drag you along as you plead for a quarter for a cup of coffee. Better yet, start a charity such as Somalians For A Smog Free China. If that doesn't start the money rolling in, nothing will.

Stealing: None of us are really that dumb, are we?

Printing press: I wouldn't recommend this method. Most counterfeiters are pretty stupid, and trying to pass twenty dollar bills that say "Glory Hallelujah" instead of "In God We Trust" will draw them twenty years in Leavenworth. Stick to printing birthday and wedding announcements.

Financial investments: I'll quote a famous authority on financial investing named Fess Buckenshaw. "If you got a buck, give half of it to someone to invest an' keep t'other half to 'et on. If yore half disappears before the half you gave the other guy, yore eatin' too much." He also says, "The only type of stock I ever invested in is the kind that wanders up to the barn to be fed every night. That way, I knowed I was assured of a guaranteed nightly return on my investment."

There are three risk levels when playing the stock market. Low risk, or blue chip stock represents the well established, constant growth companies. They can fail only if the North American continent breaks away and floats westward toward Japan. Moderate risk stocks are a mix of dynamic growth domestic companies and international ventures controlled by foreign terrorists and dictators. They are reasonably safe until someone's grenade accidentally goes off in a board meeting. High risk stocks are for the brave of heart. Beware of anyone trying to get you to invest in the oil well being sunk in Mohammed Yomama Sahid's back yard. Also, stay away from any claim of superior cotton being grown in the Swiss Alps.

The greatest single investment anyone will ever make is a home. If your combined family income is at least $100,000, you may qualify to purchase a home in the $25,000-$30,000 range. If you earn $200,000 or more annually, you can expect to afford such luxuries as a garage and a back yard. Without going into your total investment at payoff, suffice it to say you will have put out enough to buy the entire country of Bulgaria in turn of the century dollars. Don't worry about not having a garage. Statistics say that your new car will be stolen within a month anyway.

Money matters finally divide into two general categories. Making more and keeping what you already have. Nowadays, doing either can be difficult since the two can be closely entwined, especially when you receive an offer to "watch your savings grow from a minimum investment." The only sure "growth" comes from plenty of fertilizer applied to a lawn. But who wants to encourage growth in something that needs to be mowed every week?

As for me, I'll stick with putting my money into developing gold mines in New Jersey. The fellow told me they were within a foot if hitting the big vein and my money would supply just the right amount of blood. I haven't heard from them in a while, but he told me that the newest shaft would be named after my trust and faith in the project, The Push It In and Twist. Kind of has a classy ring to it, don't you think?

BUILDING PECS, ABS, AND HERNIAS

(These days, a person is sometimes judged by his or her appearance. Seems like kind of a moot point when the guy holding a gun under the nose of the convenience store clerk has well developed biceps and is wearing a custom made suit.)

Silence hung like a shroud over the assembly of watchers, broken occasionally by a muted, "yeah man, c'mon, you can do it. Focus!"

I barely noticed the encouragement as I began mentally channeling the power of my tense, muscular body, starting at the tips of my toes, feeling it grow as my rippling leg, thigh, and upper torso muscles began to tingle in a rush of adrenalin. Building, building, the strength began to flow to my arms as I bent to grasp the bar.

The massive black weights loomed like wagon wheels in the periphery of my vision. As my resin coated hands gripped the steel shaft, my mind narrowed to a single hot, searing point, my entire being concentrated on the task at hand.

A guttural growl began forming at the bottom of my chest and grew to a howl as I sent all my energy into the lift. With explosive force I jerked – and tore the headboard off the bed.

I rushed back to reality as the adoring screams of the crowd were replaced by Judy standing at the foot of the bed waving her ball bat and shouting, "Put it down, put it down. Slowwwly, slowwwly – that's a good boy."

I tried to explain to her - as I re-attached the headboard – that I have been concerned about my lack of physical exercise, and that the dream no doubt resulted from my need to remedy the situation. To emphasize the point, I tried making a muscle, causing her to bring the bat back into a defensive position.

When nothing even resembling a muscle appeared on my arm, she lowered the bat and collapsed in a fit of laughter, pointing at the arm and gasping something about seeing bigger biceps on a banana. That did it!

A few days later, we (Judy and I) paid our money to a local health institute and started working out on a demonic device that incorporates a number of exercises involving lifting weights with arms, legs, and even eyebrows. Attached to this thing were weights that I think were meant to be gripped by the teeth to build jaw muscles that would let you hold back a car by clamping onto the bumper with your lips. With this mechanical marvel, one can perform a bench press, curls, leg press, jerks (a fitting term), eyeball bulgers, tooth grinders, eyebrow wrinklers, arch flatteners and hernia poppers.

I faced the thing on the first session remembering being told, "After working out five hours a day for only four years, even you can have stunning abs and pecs." I wouldn't know an ab or a pec from a rusty manhole cover, but I swore that if

I didn't have those within the allotted time, the person who said I would had better have a one-way bus ticket to Mexico City in his pocket.

My wife's reason for working out were two-fold. First, she has been slowing down in her reaction time with the bat. She almost didn't get out of the way in time when I came close to throwing a night table on her while I dreamt I was Wyatt Earp saddling a horse.

Secondly, she's getting tired of listening to my excuses for why I can't help her move the kitchen appliances at spring cleaning time. Soon (I had hopes), she'd be able to hold up the refrigerator while I sweep under it.

Being appropriately dressed for pumping iron is important if one is to be comfortable and acceptable to other grunt and groaners. Usually, loose fitting sweat pants, a sweat shirt, kidney belt, hernia and neck brace, and steel arch supports symbolize the savvy lifter. I included wrist wraps and knee pads for those times when it's necessary to fall to your hands and knees in exhaustion while yelling, "Get this @#^&% thing off my neck."

The recommended procedure for a beginner is to start with weights that can be lifted at least ten times without putting a major strain on your carotid artery or the large intestine. If one blows, you die. If the other one blows, you die of embarrassment. For someone like me, who after long winter months is barely able to lift his feet off the floor, this meant about twenty pounds.

To keep track of my progress, I weighed myself before starting. As the droopy parts turn to muscle, which is more dense than flab, a weight gain means progress is being made.

Standing in front of the full length mirror provided for those who need to admire their physique, I gazed for the last time at the 6 foot, 3 inch, 160 pound wreck that until now wouldn't wear a bathing suit in public without a full length trench coat. Soon, I would be able to face public nakedness with confidence and the assurance that I would no longer be the subject of ridicule and scorn.

Forty-five minutes later, I stood on rubbery legs in front of the same mirror and stared at a changed man. My bloodshot eyes stared back from hollow pits while my jaw hung slack and useless.

Hair that looked like an explosion in a mattress factory hung over my forehead while everything from my eyeballs to the last molecule in my toenails felt like they had been used in automobile crash tests. Wobbling to the scales, I wailed in despair as it settled on 160 pounds.

Where were all the heavier muscles I had worked so hard for? "Don't worry, dear," said Judy. "It takes time. In six months you'll notice a big difference in the way you look and feel."

"Do you mean in six months I could look like Charles Atlas?" I moaned.

Helping me off the scales, she walked me to a bench and lowered me onto it. With sympathy in her voice, she said, "You're not body building. This is for exercise and muscle tone. Besides, Charles Atlas has been dead for years."

"That's what I mean," I snarled. "If I keep this up for six months, I'll look just like him."

Subsequent visits saw a lessening of the torture, but I finally decided it was time to consult with an expert. My son-in-law, a long time competitive power lifter, was offering a part-time service in the correct methods of assaulting yourself. Since I had moved up to 30 pound weights, it was time to let him take over and direct my activities. Frankly, I felt I would be the perfect role model for him to present to his clients as the best example of the results of following the proper procedures in physical conditioning.

I envisioned the results. TODAY – ARNOLD STANG. TOMORROW – ARNOLD SCHWARZENNAGER.

Somehow, I had the feeling that I was going to have a hard time selling him on the idea.

As I stood before him in leotards, the kind with a single strap across the shoulder, tennis shoes, and an old T-shirt, he examined me closely while quietly muttering something about suicide missions. Finally, he sighed and asked if I wouldn't rather consider posing for the "before" example in a popular body building ad, rather than risk the chance for at least that distinction. As kindly as he could he related the old sayings of turning lead into gold or a sows ear into a silk purse.

I could take a hint. A muscular form isn't the only important asset for social acceptance in this world. I would take banjo lessons and push Earl Skruggs out of the picture with my rendition of Foggy Mountain Breakdown. In fact, I knew I was on my way when I had a dream that night about standing center stage in Nashville.

Unfortunately, an adoring young lady leaped onstage and began smothering me in kisses. I was jerked out of it by a baseball bat being waved under my nose and a voice hissing, "Alright you fink, who is she?"

Dan Graves

PIECE OF HAM OR A THIGH – NO THANKS

(For some people, it doesn't matter how they get their food. That is, as long as it comes in a can or they don't have to look it in the eye before they pull the trigger.)

Recently, a friend of mine related a story about his grandparents, who after spending many years in a large city, decided to return in retirement to their real love – life on the farm.

They moved into a house on ten acres that had no running water or electricity. Water came from a hand pump at the well and light from oil lamps. Although she was blind, his grandmother tended a garden by feel and cooked over a wood stove while his grandfather took care of the livestock and other necessities of life.

Once a year the back seat was removed from an old Desoto and a new calf was hauled to the farm (when Desoto ceased production the calves suffered the indignity of riding in a Chevrolet Biscayne).

Hams and sides of bacon were salt cured and hung from rodent-proof wires in the smokehouse while perishables

132

were canned and stored for the winter. Leftover table scraps were dumped into a slop jar along with dishwater to feed the hogs. No doubt the flavor of Tide added just the right bouquet to the hogs' dining pleasure.

Having had past experience, his grandparents re-adapted easily to such a lifestyle. But what about those of us whose only exposure to such a strict existence has been watching old re-runs of Green Acres or the opening scenes from The Beverly Hillbillies?

Could us city slickers survive if we were required to adapt to such a life, or would we perish like night crawlers on a hot sidewalk?

For answers, I decided to ask some of the rare handful of people who have lived such a life, questions on how to convert a hay burner into steaks, or field corn into something that doesn't stick to the roof of your mouth.

With most of the old secrets and knowledge of self-sufficiency passing into history along with those who used them, the task of finding such people can be frustrating.

Equally discouraging is the language barrier that exists between today's generation and yesterday's – as I soon discovered.

Since providing food seemed to be the item with the highest priority, I approached that first with the plan to delve into such things as clothing and shelter later. The following conversation was with an old-timer and should enlighten those who are considering abandoning frozen chicken breast patties and garden vegetables fresh from Argentina.

"You raised or grew your own food, didn't you?"

"Yup."

"Did you feel you were getting all the nutritional requirements as well as controlling your fat intake and cholesterol levels without the potentially harmful effects of alleged carcinogenic food preservation compounds?"

(Blank stare while he watched me closely to see if green tendrils would begin sprouting from my forehead.)

"Let me re-phrase that question. You're 100 years old, aren't you?"

"Yup."

"Question answered. Tell me, how do you go about dressing out a hog?"

(Another blank stare.) He finally blinked and answered, "Depends on the day of the week. Saturdays, they kinda liked to dress casual. Sunday mornin' and they insisted on starched collars and a bow tie. Rest of the week, we just put galoshes on 'em so they could keep the mud out from between their toes."

"No, I mean how did you clean a hog – you know – get them ready to eat?"

(Another stare while his hand inched slowly toward his cane). "Ain't easy. Had to keep 'em in the tub long enough to give 'em a good scrubbin'. Don't do no good, no-how. They just git out and git dirty agin in no time unless it's on Sunday mornin'. They was real careful not to git them starched collars dirty. Besides, they don't care how dirty they git afore eatin'."

"No, no. I want to know how you make them into bacon and sausage. You know, food."

"Why'nt you say that in the first place? I thought you slipped on somethin' comin' up here and fell on your head, what with talkin' about givin' 'em baths and puttin' clothes on 'em. First, you gotta make 'em dead. Number of ways to do that. Best way is to take this big sledge hammer and— ——."

He waited until I returned from throwing up my socks to continue. "Kinda tetchy, ain't ya? We'll skip that part of it. Next, ya hang the carcass up by its heels and take this big knife and————."

Once again I staggered back to my chair as he slowly slid his cane into a better position to swing it if the need arose.

"Next thing, ya throw the whole danged carcass in a vat of boiling water and commence to scrape off all the hair, and————."

With my head between my knees I gasped for air while motioning for him to continue. He scooted his chair back as if a leper had just offered to give him mouth-to-mouth resuscitation.

"You all right, boy? I guess you ain't had much experience in such matters. Kindly keep your head pointed in the other direction 'til I'm finished if you don't mind. After that, you start to slice off the ————."

"Hold it, hold it", I gasped. I don't like ham or bacon or sausage anyway. Can we get on to something else, like how to clean a chicken?" I figured knocking off a barnyard bird would be a lot less traumatic.

"Son, you are persistent. Let me set you straight. You clean a fish, butcher a hog, and pluck a chicken. Now, the first thing you do is take a sharp hatchet or axe————."

I'd had it. I jumped up and screamed, "Haven't you people ever heard of a shotgun, or maybe a garden hose attached to the exhaust pipe of a car and run into the chicken coop at midnight? What's with all these axes and sharp knives and vats of boiling water? Sounds like Monday morning at the inquisition."

He leaped out of his rocker and began jabbing at me with the cane while shouting, "HEEYA – BACK, BACK

– GIT IN THE BARN. MA, FETCH ME THE CATTLE PROD."

I cleared the porch steps in one leap and broke the four minute mile three times on the run back to town. Later that night, after sneaking back to get my car, I stopped in town and bought a Coke and a package of Twinkies, content now to be a confirmed vegetarian for life. Who needs to be self-sufficient? After all, we live in a world of frozen t.v. dinners and microwave ovens. Still, I wonder what would have happened if I had asked him how to skin a raccoon.

AGE WRINKLES – NAW, I'VE JUST GOT A LITTLE EXTRA SKIN

(One of the benefits of getting older is that you can take your teeth out, drop them by the dentist in the morning, go about your daily business and pick them up in the afternoon. It works if you don't mind looking like you've been eating green persimmons for a while.)

While trying to tie my shoelaces, I noticed that if my arms weren't getting shorter, my legs were definitely getting longer. I also considered, but quickly dispelled the idea that I may not be as limber as I used to be. Agreed, it's been a while since I've been able to put the sole of my foot on the back of my neck, but having to pull my socks on with vegetable tongs is ridiculous.

While pondering the problem, I thought of how we change as we progress through the various stages of life. As newborns, we're totally helpless, depending on adults for our every need. As time passes, we learn what a mess we've gotten into, but we also know that the adult of our species can be trained to respond to our every need if properly stimulated with, say, an ear piercing scream.

However, by the time we reach the age of three, we've added one important lesson to our philosophy of "ride 'em hard and put 'em away wet". When you push the big ones too hard, they can become violent.

The standard beating could occur from something so trivial as your mother finding the chickens looking like survivors of a Nazi death camp after not having been fed for a week. The air would be split with your full name being shrieked from the coop, followed with an order to present yourself, front and center, immediately.

Your big mistake would be to shout back, "Whaddaya want?" This would normally be followed by a series of high pitched wailings that signaled her now knowing why the eggs were being laid without a yolk and that you had less than 10 seconds to make an appearance. Like a whipped cur dog, you showed up with your hands covering your bum and whimpering the only excuse that ever came to mind at such moments.

"I forgot."

Such episodes instilled in you a grudging respect for adult authority and a firm resolve to come up with more sophisticated excuses in the future.

On your 13th birthday, a relay in your brain closed and turned you into an alien being, both unable and unwilling to communicate with anyone over the age of 22. You became a learned authority on everything and totally immune to any form of adult discipline or guidance. Conversation with "the enemy" was reduced to a series of shoulder shrugs, casting your eyes toward the ceiling, and an occasional grunt of "I dunno", or, "in a minute." Where, before this monumental birthday, you had to be held at gunpoint to keep you out of the car every time it moved, even when it was being put into the garage, you now wouldn't be seen in public with your parents if your hair was on fire and they both had fire extinguishers.

During these teen years, you learned a foreign language and adopted a bizarre dress code that elicited such comments from your parents as, "What did you say?", or, "What are you doing every night. Breaking into the Salvation Army store?" This phase lasts for 19 years and then you become – nobody.

The age of 20 is terrible. You're still too young to blow all the money your great grandmother left to you in trust, and since you're almost officially an adult, you can no longer be trusted by teens. For one year you drift around like a boat without an anchor, with your only friends being other 20 year-olds. Too young to drink, old enough to know better, and too broke to afford it.

If you're lucky enough to survive until the 21st birthday, the relay that closed at 13 pops open in your brain and directs all the synaptic activity into the "Oh, My gosh, I've gotta start making a living on my own" module, located right next to the "I don't have to work because I'm just a kid" module. Suddenly, you feel like a bullfighter with an anvil in his back pocket. Having survived 12 years in grade and high school and probably four more in college, you would have changed your mind about a career more often than a horsefly at the Kentucky Derby.

At last, your parents breathe a sigh of relief as you announce that their $100,000 spent on your education has landed you a job as an assistant dishwasher at a local hash house. Now, you can make your own car payments, if you can find someone who will sell you a car complete with an engine for $30 or less.

The years pass and you advance to head dishwasher, then to manager, and finally you own the joint. Life is comfortable in your three bedroom ranch, complete with a two-car garage and a yard full of moles.

Then one morning a gray hair sags down between your eyes and fifteen minutes later you're at the drugstore sorting through the hair care products. Self-consciously, you explain to the clerk that it's to hide a spot on the back of your dog in time for the canine show next week. Next comes dozens of bottles of vitamins and minerals, skin care products and daily 10 mile runs, and belts pulled so tight you look like a Coke bottle and your legs turn purple from lack of circulation.

Eventually, you graduate from reading glasses from the Dollar Store to bifocals, you couldn't hear a grenade going off in your pocket, and you've ordered dentures from a mail order firm that advertises, one size fits all. Gone are the days of free spending. Now, you wouldn't pay a nickel to watch an ant eat a bale of hay.

Finally, the straw is added that breaks the camel's back. A grandchild says, "Paps, you are one way-out, cool dude, but the digs are sick and the threads are sub-standard. Get with it and chill out."

Now it's your turn! Spit your dentures out, rip off your tri-focals, turn down your hearing aid and shout, "Why, you young whippersnapper! I'm just as rooty as you and I can still cut a pretty mean rug. Poo-Poo-Pe-Doo and twenty-three skidoo to you."

Life goes on.

THE COLONISTS RETURN TO THE MOTHERLAND

(We may have whupped them back then, but they got revenge by selling us those dinky little cars that fell apart faster than a rat running up a banana tree.)

I used to be a fan of those flashy little sports cars imported from the European Continent, having owned a number of the tiny rust buckets, all well used by the time I acquired them. After a few years of such folly, I became used to them spending more time in the garage than on the road, although I was grateful to them for expanding my already vast knowledge of four-letter expletives.

When friends asked if my wife and I would like to accompany them on a tour of England and Scotland, I saw my chance for revenge. What the Axis powers failed to accomplish in WW2 I would finish, especially as far as the English car company, British Leland was concerned. I'd teach them to mess around with a Yankee rebel.

The four of us, carrying enough luggage to sink a small ocean-going vessel departed for the first stop in Atlanta where we boarded a flight for Manchester, England. As darkness fell, we flew north along the east coast, peering through the darkness as the lights of Washington, D.C., New York, and other cities passed beneath in a seemingly unbroken chain. Our course took us over Nova Scotia and Labrador, then east across the Atlantic.

Gazing out the windows at midnight, we witnessed one of nature's grandest spectacles. The northern lights, illuminating the sky with an eerie glow, stretched from horizon to horizon as tendrils of green and white hung like wisps of glowing fire, illuminating the clouds below in what looked like multi-colored moonlight. I fell asleep with my nose pressed against the window.

Bright light pried one eye and then the other open as we flew on into the rising sun. I pinched my nose back into its original shape while pulling my tongue off the roof of my mouth where it had stuck like a bug on a windshield. The breakfast served to us innocent prisoners tasted like something scraped off the floor of Buck's Garage. My south end, having been planted in one spot for hours, had given up on receiving its fair share of the blood supply, leaving me feeling like I was sitting on a lump of clay.

After what seemed like a century of flying over the, no doubt shark infested waters of the Atlantic, we spotted land through the cloud layer below. I tried to cheer, but all that came out was a croak when I was informed that we were over the Emerald Isle and that the sea of Ireland and its sharks had to be crossed before we made landfall in England. Knowing we had to be ominously close to running out of fuel, I donned the life preserver supplied with each seat and inflated it.

Explaining to the flight attendant that I was deathly afraid of sharks did little to appease her, especially after the thing had pushed my wife from her seat. It was humiliating to have the attendant stand by my seat for the remainder of the flight, scowling at me like an irate parent with an undisciplined child. I considered writing a letter to the airline suggesting they include a shark repellant, preferably a shotgun with each seat pack life preserver.

At last, merry Olde England arrived under us and we gazed down on patch work quilt fields in various shades of green bordered by stone walls, no doubt erected to keep sheep in and tourists out. Such barriers would do them no good as I fully intended to exact my revenge on those makers of cute but shoddy automobiles.

At Manchester, we de-planed and stood before customs officers looking like Mongolians on their very worst day. Unshaven, with red, swollen eyes from lack of sleep, clothing disheveled and resembling remnants from a fire at the Salvation Army and struggling with 500 pounds of luggage each, the officials decided it would be simpler to attack Russia than search us for contraband. After mumbling something about their previous attempts to civilize our country being a failure, they waved us through.

Since it seemed appropriate to our image, each of us adopted a moniker: Billy The Kid, James Dalton, Calamity Jane, and Cow Patty. We drug our luggage through the terminal toward the car rental agency and the beginning of what would prove to be the most challenging part of the trip. The English drive little cars with the steering wheel on the wrong side and then compound the problem by driving on the wrong side of the road. We were issued a bright red Vauxhall with only 11 miles on the odometer and a manual transmission that had the shift lever located on, again, the wrong side. After stuffing our luggage and ourselves aboard and waving to the crowd that had collected to watch their idea of the Beverly Hillbillies, we attacked the unsuspecting motorists of England.

Since Billy The Kid and myself were the insured drivers, we assumed the task of learning how to shift gears and somehow survive the trip to Barnoldswick, our base of operations, north of Manchester. Billy was elected to drive and we left the terminal, ricocheting off curbs and forcing pedestrians to seek whatever cover was available.

"No, no, left lane!"

"What does that sign mean?"

"How am I supposed to know?"

"Shut up so I can concentrate."

"I see they use that gesture over here, too."

After negotiating a number of round-a-bouts which are circular intersections for routing traffic onto the desired roads, we floundered onto a motorway, their equivalent of our interstates, only slightly more insane. Six lanes wide with a center median separating the opposing race tracks, the scene to us was chaotic. A speed limit of 70 miles per hour was apparently selected only as an arbitrary figure to satisfy some special interest group.

The inside lane is used by lorries (trucks) and drivers over the age of 90. The middle lane is reserved for daring tourists and student drivers who feel comfortable at 80 miles per hour with another vehicle following less than six feet behind. The outside lane is used by the Starship Enterprise crowd at speeds of warp factor 4 and above. If you encounter someone traveling only 75 in the middle lane, the decision must be made to pull into the starship lane while trying to coax an overloaded Vauxhall around the laggard. There, you face the possibility of being flattened into road kill by Buck Rogers on his way to Mars. All of this with the driver in the right side seat combined with three screaming passengers had us wondering why we hadn't opted for a couple of relaxing weeks in Rollercoaster Land U.S.A, instead.

In order to reach Barnoldswick, a small village in rural northern England, we had to exit the six lane mayhem and experience the other two types of roadways calmly referred to on our map as A and B roads. A description of these will come later, but suffice it to say we welcomed the return to the super sleds in future travels.

Arriving at Barnoldswick we managed to find our lodgings, a quaint old farm home that resembled a Currier and Ives print, complete with stone fences and the typical sheep grazing in green fields around it. We learned quickly where to step, because these wooly assassins had free access to the grounds and weren't backward about marking their presence.

We collapsed after so many hours without rest and awoke the next morning refreshed and ready for our first day of sightseeing. I fixed coffee and retired to the courtyard to gaze down on the town and wait for the others to pry their eyes open. The old stone home, sitting on a hill overlooking the town was surrounded by colorful flowers and neatly trimmed shrubs. Cattle mooed and sheep bleated in the adjoining pastures while a strange type of dove cooed in the trees. Ravens (crows to us) flew overhead as the rising sun turned the clouds to gold. In the distance, rolling hills were cloaked in a blue haze that softened the surrounding countryside, a quiltwork of fields separated by ancient looking stone fences and hedgerows.

Suddenly, at the gate to the courtyard there appeared three characters we soon dubbed Larry, Moe, and Curly Joe. Darting quick glances around, these three buffoons of the sheep colony invited themselves in. By now, the rest of my companions had joined me, so Rosie (her real name) and I hitched up our gun belts, saddled the horses and began the round-up. Our hostess had requested that we not leave the gate open to avoid livestock around the house, and seeing it ajar, the sneaky rascals were licking their lips as they eyed the flower beds.

With a few hand slaps and geehaws, we had the sweater crowd on the run, their plump rumps bounding down the lane. Thereafter, we enjoyed coming home to find those three standing in the drive, their beady yellow eyes reflecting a combined IQ of 20 and a determination to gain access to the courtyard and its selection of tasty geraniums.

Our first destination was York, known for its Old York, a 500 year-old shopping center, and York Minster, an ancient church of immense proportions and grandeur. The drive, a distance of 50 miles, was a mix of admiring the countryside and stark terror caused by driving 60 miles per hour on the wrong side of the narrow roads. To add to the difficulty, we occasionally passed triangular signs with a picture of a cow on them. Nothing was more confidence inspiring than knowing that not only were you risking everyone's life by driving a car with the steering wheel where the passenger should be, but that at any moment you could be sharing your lane with a herd of Holsteins. In fact, on two occasions we stopped at traffic signals on cattle crossings while a farmer drove his herd across the road. Now, when I see stop lights, visions of fresh milk and a hamburger cross my mind.

At York, a fair sized city, we wound through narrow, crooked streets, our rear view mirrors barely missing other cars and pedestrians. Finally, a public parking lot appeared where I sat gripping the wheel, clicking my heels together and muttering, "there's no place like home, there's no place like home." The others pried me out of the car and threatened to buy one of those funny looking English driving caps and make me wear it if I didn't get my act together.

Wiping tears from my eyes and with spittle drooling from the corner of my mouth I followed them into Old York. The original buildings, dating back to a time when clothing was unique, had been converted to numerous shops while retaining some of their air of antiquity. The only items not offered for sale were banjos and Red Man chewing tobacco. Since we didn't have time to cover the whole area, I'm not sure about those. Throngs of people crowded the streets, some of them still cobblestone (the streets, that is) while musicians and sand painters demonstrated their talents in exchange for a donation of "a bob or two".

I had a fair amount of English change in my pocket, but I soon found out that bigger isn't always better. Their ten pence coin would choke a horse while the one pound coin wouldn't make a decent splash in a tea cup. To avoid embarrassment when making a purchase, I would hold out a handful of coins and act like a hillbilly fresh off the boat. The merchant would select the ones he needed and smile at me with pity and compassion. It was fun to grin at him or her and say, "Whooee, I shore thank'e pard. Y'All take care now, y'here."

Not only do Americans have an image to uphold, it was worth it to watch their expressions over this assault on the English language. Within a few days, all four of us were confidently counting out the correct amount without holding up the line for more than ten minutes.

York Minster proved to be worth the trip in itself. Two city blocks long and bristling with towers and spires that rose hundreds of feet, intricate and beautiful stone works and stain glass windows sparkling in the sunlight, it represented a tribute to the masterful work and capabilities of the architects of centuries ago. That such a structure could be built before our present mechanized age seemed impossible.

Though the view from outside was awe inspiring, the interior was stunning, leaving one with a feeling of insignificance and wonder. Massive columns supported Gothic arch ceilings adorned with delicate filigree, while stories high stained glass windows cast multi-colored rainbows into the vastness of the sanctuary. Delicate stone carvings of English monarchs flanked the base of a towering pipe organ while adjoining rooms and alcoves displayed other carvings and tombs of past nobility.

Construction began on this marvelous structure in 1220 with one stained glass window dating from the 13th century. One could only stand and stare in silence as the white and gold arched ceilings extended into the distance, flanked by the works in wood, stone, and metal of many skilled artisans of long ago. Such a sight makes our modern structures seem cheap and tawdry by comparison, superior only in their height and the amount of Windex they consume.

Reluctantly, we left for the journey back to Barnoldswick. If driving in daylight was stressful, we couldn't imagine the trip being made after dark. Since it was now Bill's turn to drive, the rest of us secured our seatbelts, divided up the loose coats and whatever else would serve as shock absorbers, wrapped them around ourselves and struck up a lively chorus of the 23rd psalm. We made it back without bent fenders or fear induced potty stops. It was now time to practice our "Hoot Mon's" and "Woo'y be a McGregor or a McKinley" in preparation for the trip north to kilts and old castles in Scotland.

Now that we had survived two full days of driving in England, we informed the police escort that had been assigned full time to us during our stay that we would like to visit Scotland. After a two hour delay while the queen, who had requested to be informed of our whereabouts in the interest of national security decided whether the traffic system of their northern neighbor could withstand an international incident, we were on our way to Edinburgh and the Tattoo.

The Tattoo is an annual event of international renown, featuring military bands from a number of countries as well as performances by Scottish dancers and re-enactments of historical events in Scottish and English history. Also represented were the famous (or infamous) characters who caused the ruckus in the first place. Leaving our escort at the border, we crossed into the birthplace of golf, kilts, and Scotch whiskey.

One small incident still stands out in our memory that typifies the saying, "Ya' only be as auld as ye feel, especially behind the wheel." Buzzing along at 75 miles per hour while grinding our teeth into dust particles and wiping fear sweat from our brows, we were passed by a car doing 90 that looked like a prize from a cereal box.

Sitting behind the wheel, casually steering with one hand was a little, old lady who looked like she was old enough to remember when Mark Twain had been the hot topic. With her white head barely visible in the windshield, she disappeared in the distance while we all agreed that maybe there was hope for us in the future after all.

In Edinburgh, we once again faced crowded, narrow lanes with no idea how to find Edinburgh castle where the show would take place. We drove along streets lined on either side by stone buildings that looked ancient, stained black by accumulations of centuries of coal smoke, their intricate carvings, spires, and delicate window and door arches reflecting a city that thrived during a time when we were still trying to convince the Indians that $29 was an exorbitant price to pay for Manhattan Island.

Finally, in the distance we spied a formidable structure sitting high atop a stone cliff, its battlements affording a commanding view of the entire city. We concluded that this had to be either Edinburgh Castle or the corporate headquarters of McDonald's. Fewer that ten minor traffic incidents later, we stood looking up at what has to rank as one of the major architectural achievements of its time.

Built on a stone monolith of grand proportions, the castle's walls seemed like extensions of the cliffs reaching far above our heads. Battlements and turrets abound, while the muzzles of numerous old cannon protruded from the walls, warning potential invaders that conquering it would be about as simple as eating a fully grown oak tree.

A long walk through bustling streets past buildings of picture post card charm and antiquity led us to the entrance of the castle parade grounds where we joined the line waiting for entry.

As darkness fell the castle was lit with various colored floodlights while torches burned along the battlements and walkways atop the walls. The parade ground suddenly plunged into darkness as floodlights were extinguished. Huge wooden doors at the entrance to the grounds slowly swung open revealing a wall of man-made fog illuminated by lights from within the entranceway.

Like ghosts from a medieval time, the Queens Own Highlanders, over 100 strong, their bagpipes shrilling and drums rattling, marched from the mist and onto the grounds, followed by bands from England, Scotland, France, and Egypt. Colored light again emblazoned the grounds as cannon roared from the embattlements. Thrilled at the sight and sounds of such a magnificent beginning, I fought down the urge to stand and shout, "God Save The Queen." That would have probably been the first time in its history that a Yankee was ejected from the Tattoo.

There followed two hours of music, traditional dancing, and enactments of Scottish and English history, complete with period costumes and magnificent horses. All too soon it was over and we tackled the task of finding our way to our lodgings in Dalkeith, a suburb of Edinburgh, in the dark. Earlier in the day we had located the home, a mid-19th century stone structure complete with formal gardens and a carriage house, after only a little bit of inconvenience.

Truthfully, we had come upon it after about the same amount of trouble experienced by Hannibal as he drove a herd of elephants across the Alps. Feeling confident that we were within a short distance of our goal, we entered a roundabout and chose the wrong exit. Turning back, we entered the same roundabout and made two circuits, unable to decide which was the correct exit. After much shouting and general hub-bub we exited again. Wrong again.

Back to the roundabout. By this time other motorists were beginning to recognize us and were waving as we passed. We had hoped that one of them might volunteer to foot the bill for a late snack while giving us directions, but they left us to our own devices. Finally on what we assumed was the correct street, we crept along, backing up traffic, no doubt collecting a few four-letter words in the native language from the other motorists. The correct address finally appeared and Dalkeith traffic returned to its normal state of chaos.

The home, built as usual from weathered stone, was beyond all our expectations of what we envisioned a typical Scottish manor would look like. Built in 1856 by a prominent doctor, it stood three stories tall and was surrounded by manicured floral gardens entwined around trees that looked as old as the house. Walking paths leading to a carriage house wound through this tapestry of color.

Inside, the 19th century décor included vaulted ceilings with intricate scroll work in raised relief, polished brass and colorful antique porcelain bathroom fixtures, floral mosaic patterned floors and a large curly-haired dog lying by the fireplace in the formal sitting room.

Hot tea, cakes and cookies were waiting for us, and as we sat admiring the surroundings, the dog took an interest in my cookie. I watched him just as intently, but I soon learned that one does not take his eye off a Scottish hound, especially one with a sweet tooth.

Turning to speak to my wife resulted in a large, black muzzle quickly pressing against the pastry. The cook/gardener came to the rescue and led the hound from the room just as I was about to offer him tea to go with the cookie, followed by a lesson in traditional Yankee cussing. I found out later that he would have refused the tea, being a staunch whiskey drinker, instead.

After a delightful stay in a 19th century bed and breakfast, we decided to further explore Edinburgh and learn a little of Scottish traditions, including their foods. I soon learned of the cruelties that can be inflicted on unsuspecting foreigners.

Following a short sightseeing tour, we seated ourselves at a charming sidewalk café and scanned the menu. While the others ordered the usual fare of boiled mountain goat, I asked the waitress to explain the composition of a menu item called haggis, neets, and tates. With an evil grin she described it as a dish enjoyed by the Scots for generations. My philosophy is, when in Rome, do as the Romans. She served a plate of what proved to be rather tasty fare and I consumed it down to the last neet. Afterwards, she revealed that neets are turnips, tates are potatoes, and haggis is the result of skinning a sheep and running the remains through a blender, then frying the whole mess to a golden brown. I spent the next half-hour hugging a lamp post, trying not to hiccup and cause my digestive system to evacuate the premises.

Vowing not to eat anything not wrapped in a Burger King package, we left to return to England while taking a leisurely tour of back roads through the scenic countryside of Scotland. Our only scheduled stop was Borthwick Castle, noted for being the past residence of an unwilling guest in the person of Mary Queen Of Scots. Now a hotel, it ranked rather low in the order of size and grandeur, but high in historical significance. The great hall was decorated with suits of medieval armor, striking oil paintings, and wall displays of ancient weaponry. Built of (what else) stone with walls fourteen feet thick, it had withstood a long siege of cannon fire from Cromwell and his troops in the 16th century. Evidence of the bombardment remains, as a large cavity in an outside wall attests to the futility of trying to down an elephant with slingshots.

Approaching a young man, obviously an employee, I asked if the queen would be available for autographs.

"Ah, which queen wou'y be 'a wantin', sor?"

"I didn't know you had more than one, but I'd prefer Mary. If she's not available, we'll take whichever one happens to be on duty."

"But sor, she 'a bein' deid."

I was stunned. I finally managed to ask where the funeral was being held so we could pay our respects. He looked at me like I was leper offering him a drink from my beer bottle

"She's 'a bein' deid for over four hundred years."

He apparently lost interest in the conversation when I asked if she had paid her bill before checking out.

Continuing south, we followed narrow, winding roads through rolling, low mountainous terrain, the hillsides covered with heather, giving a lavender cast to the countryside while sheep grazed around the occasional farm house. Small villages, each with its ornate church complete with needle-like spire and homes of typical Scottish charm nestled amid growths of pine and well kept flower gardens. We stopped at Stow for lunch and my first shot of genuine Scotch whiskey. It seemed like the proper thing to do since it was no doubt straight from the barrel and served on home ground.

Drinking liquor straight has never been one of my favorite sports, but by holding my nose and closing my eyes it can be a little more tolerable than walking on hot coals. Actually, it wasn't bad when sipped in small tongue wetting quantities. But now I know why the Scots were always attacking England. After a shot of that stuff, you feel like running a hundred miles and attacking something. Anything!

Pressing on we arrived in Galasheil, Scotland, a quaint town bustling with activity where the ladies spotted signs advertising genuine Scottish woolen clothing at the WHOLESALE OUTLET. For Bill and I, it was like a dash of cold water in the face. Is nothing immune to Yankee influence? For the ladies, it was a touch of home with an international flair.

For the next two hours Bill and I casually toured the town as two streaks of concentrated fury tore from store to store in pursuit of woolen bargains in the traditional weave of Scottish tartans. We considered kilts, but the thought of our scrawny, hairy legs hanging out of skirts gave us cold chills. This, coupled with the bagpipes we would need to complete the wardrobe would have had us shot on the town square without a trial or a formal hearing. The sound of the best by Lester Flatt and Earl Scruggs being screeched out by Laurel and Hardy in kilts would have been beyond human endurance. We would no doubt do the same thing to a Scotsman trying to play Amazing Grace on the banjo.

While browsing the main street of Galasheil, it dawned on us that none of the towns in England or Scotland have the outlying shopping centers so common in America. Their retail commerce is centered in the town just as it has always been. It was refreshing to stroll among the throngs of people and occasionally scramble up a light pole as errant motorists decided to park on the sidewalk. Such hustle and bustle pushed all thoughts of Wallace World out of our minds. After managing to corral the ladies, their pupils dilated and spittle drooling out of the corners of their mouths, we continued south where our police escort met us at the border and escorted us back to Barnoldswick.

There, one small incident left a citizen with a lasting impression of American drivers. I was at the wheel as we drove the narrow, main street through town, each side of which was lined with parked vehicles, making space even more of a premium. A lady had just parked her car and was leaning over to lock the door when I passed. From the drivers side, the distance was awkward to judge and I proceeded to wipe a few squashed bugs off the rear view mirror onto her ample bum. Sher squealed a high-pitched "Wheee" and I ducked down so as not to be easily identified should she report me to the local constable. Perhaps I should have stopped and apologized, but instead I decided to stay out of town for a while, at least long enough to think up a good disguise.

Bill and I were invited to join three of our English friends in the tradition of shooting a few rounds of sporting clays at their exclusive club, its ranges set among the rolling hills on the outskirts of Barnoldswick. Our hosts knew the sight of two Yankees dressed in Dockers would come as a shock to the other club members, so we were passed off as patients of a London mental institution out for a day of recreational therapy.

Since neither of us had any experience at shooting sporting clays or skeet, David, our mentor, stood by us (actually, 20 yards behind) and instructed us in such things as proper lead on the target, not dropping the shotgun, and not yelling "YEEHAA" when we hit a clay, or $%#@^& when we missed. Within a few minutes we had demonstrated that we couldn't hit a full grown Holstein tied to a tree and that the Indians could take back our country with ease if Bill and I were assigned to protect it.

Finishing the round, we offered to pay the going market price for the two dead sheep and for repairs to the hole in the club house roof. They politely declined on the provision that we not fire another gun while in their country. On that note we left while I recalled a famous quote from one of their best known leaders. I've re-phrased it to fit the occasion:

Never has so few done so much to so many in such a short period of time. We shall forever be mindful of the need for watchfulness."

Northbound again, this time to the Scottish Highlands and The Gathering. This event of international acclaim is held annually in the town of Braemar and is a contest that pits the skill and strength of Scottish clans in running, throwing the heavy and light hammer, tugs of war, tossing the caber, pipes and drums and dancing competitions.

After an overnight stay in Banchory, Scotland we awoke the day of the games to cold rain and dreary skies. The forty mile drive to Braemar, a small town nestled in the mountains, was an unforgettable experience of scenery that verified our expectations of the country. Dome shaped mountains rose on either side of the road as we passed through forests of tall pines and heather covered foot hills. Fingers of mist rose from the trees as we followed the winding path of the River Dee, its waters rushing about boulders and through green fields where sheep grazed contentedly. The rain and low lying overcast only added to what was a continual scene from the brushes of the world's greatest artist.

In Braemar, the Dee, a fairly wide and fast flowing stream cascaded between natural stone walls, its rush and roar adding to the pastoral scene of old stone buildings and homes that appeared to have been there since a Scotsman first fell off a bar stool.

The grounds where the games were to be held was a large, round green surrounded by bleachers with an ornate cottage on one side where Her Majesty The Queen would observe the mayhem that afternoon. As we sat on wet newspapers holding umbrellas, the first of the pipe and drum bands marched onto the field, their colors and music stirring our very souls with a rendition of Ye Doon I' Good Ya' Na' Goot Boom, I think. Other groups followed with their interpretation of what sounded like the same melody. Bagpipes are like crows. Once they're stirred up, they all sound alike.

Then began a day of frenzied activity as tug of war teams strained at the ropes, hairy gentlemen wearing kilts tossed heavy weights attached to wooden handles, while others tossed the caber as pipers marched on and off the field. Dancers in colorful period costumes swung to the Seann Truibhaas dancing competition and everyone had a great, but damp time.

The one event that draws the most attention is the Scottish tradition of tossing the caber. Practically speaking, this thing is a telephone pole that reaches a length of 19 feet, 6 inches and weighs about as much as a Volkswagen. The contestant balances it on his shoulder by holding the small end, runs forward and tosses it in an arc so that it lands on the large end and hopefully falls away from him to a position as close to straightaway as possible. Personally, I saw this as the perfect way to acquire either a prize winning hernia or a sizeable knot on the head if the thing happened to fall the wrong way. I wondered about the origin of such a bizarre sport and came to the only reasonable conclusion.

One hundred-seventy years ago (the first year of the games) a logging camp lost their mule. Someone suggested using Angus "The Bull" Gordon to load logs and ever since the other clans have been trying to prove they are as smart and strong as Angus and the mule.

The rain and cold drove us back to Banchory and our lodgings where we planned our trip the next day to the Holy Grail of golfing, St. Andrews and the world's first site of this frustrating and miserable game. Bill would have delayed picking up his lottery winnings and extra day just to walk on the hallowed grounds of Old St. Andrews golf course. As for me, I was out for revenge of some sort against the maniac who invented the game. When we arrived and entered the grand old clubhouse, I spoke with an official and rather austere looking gentleman.

"Could you direct me to the office of the personage responsible for this insane, er, fine pastime, sir?

His eyes widened as he replied, "I'm sorry, sor, but he's a' bein' deid for aboot four hundred years now."

Shocked once more, I asked if he had been hanging around with Mary Queen Of Scots when he met his untimely demise. Puzzled by his animosity, I tried to conceal the can of spray paint behind my back as I inquired as to where the gentleman was planted so that I might pay my respects. His refusal left me no choice but to spray "Kilroy Was Here" on the restroom wall of the oldest golf club in the world.

We will always remember with fondness such places as Bolton Abby, Warwick Castle, Skipton Castle, and Harewood House. Also, a kind old gentleman who was the warden of an eleventh century church that is seldom seen by foreign visitors, as well as a host of other sights and scenes of beautiful countryside and ancient architecture that cannot be matched for its charm and human history. But most of all, we were grateful to Larry, Moe, and Curly Joe for not damaging the geraniums when we carelessly left the courtyard gate open.

THE GREAT OUTDOORS – OR IS IT?

(Deer hunters possess some very special qualities. One of them is the ability to convince themselves that sitting up a tree in freezing weather for hours makes them smarter than their quarry.)

Every year hoards of hunters brush the dust off their equipment, smear themselves with foul-smelling fake scents, don their jungle camouflage, shoulder their trusty shootin' arns and head for the woods where they hang for hours on a stand nailed up a tree, twenty feet off the ground, with the hope of bagging the elusive white tail deer.

According to statistics, we are presently plagued with over-population of this species and a thinning of the herd is necessary to avoid having them grazing on the courthouse lawn or bouncing off the headlights of our SUV's. To meet this challenge, legions of courageous hunters subject themselves to conditions that would cause even the toughest Neanderthal to swear off hunting and take up gardening.

A good example is bow hunters. Having purchased a bow capable of shooting down a satellite and a brace of arrows that would give Attila The Hun nightmares, they struggle out of bed in the wee hours, think nothing of driving miles through blizzards and other foul weather and spend hours sitting in a tree stand where they eventually fall asleep, waiting for a quarry that wouldn't come out on such a day, even to watch the hunter fall out of the tree.

As a safety measure against falling and impaling themselves on the razor bladed arrows, they attach a safety line to themselves. Therefore, the only injury is to their pride when another hunter finds them dangling ten feet from the ground, asleep.

As dawn breaks, they sit motionless, looking like Bolivian freedom fighters on a budget, their senses keen for the slightest sound or movement, until they fall asleep.

The theory behind a tree stand is that deer never look up.

Baloney! I used my brother-in-law's stand one day to observe the local deer population, with the hopes of getting some photographs without the "Dan'l Boone's Petting Zoo" sign in the background. Three does suddenly appeared, looked up at me and turned in a better time than Don "The Snake" Prudhomme ever produced in his top fuel dragster. Maybe that's the reason more trees than deer are killed with arrows. I couldn't hit an eighty-car freight train from ten feet away with a bow, much less a creature that can go from a dead stop to light speed in less than five seconds. Unfortunately, many "buck fevered" hunters try it anyway, resulting in the game being wounded, only to die later.

My first and last attempt at deer hunting proved more valuable in carefully choosing your hunting companions than it did in outfoxing one of those wily critters. I had never attempted to bag anything larger than a squirrel, so when a friend invited me and two other escapees from the funny farm to join him at his uncle's cabin for a night of merriment to be followed by a day of hunting, we jumped at the chance.

Properly armed and attired in the latest fashions we headed for what our host described as "a cabin so far out that even carrier pigeons get lost". As the ignorant led the ignorant, we wondered what to do with a deer should we bag one.

"We'll cook and eat it there," said retard #1.

"But, don't we have to skin it first?" asked #2.

"Naw,"said #3 (me), "they're covered with hair, so we'll set it on fire, let it burn for an hour and Bingo, cooked venison." So, on a late winter afternoon, loaded with a provision bag containing a bottle of ketchup and a loaf of bread in anticipation of venison burgers, we left civilization for an evening in what we visualized as a rustic river chalet and tomorrow's big hunt.

To say the cabin was isolated was an understatement. When any semblance of the dirt road and then a discernable trail disappeared, I asked the criminal whose uncle owned the real estate if his uncle had used imported material for construction, or had he built it from locally available mud and sticks. "He's still putting a few finishing touches on it," came the reply, "but you'll be surprised at how well it's built." A sense of foreboding came over me as we stumbled through darkening woods in a howling wind that peppered us with ice balls and snow. I didn't like that answer.

As the gloom deepened to near total darkness, we slid into a small clearing and faced our lodging. Simultaneously, three of us dropped to our knees, extended our arms skyward and cried, "Why us, Lord? Why did you let us make the acquaintance of this nephew of a disciple of the devil?" With that we fell forward on our faces in the snow and wept while whimpering, "If you don't strike him now, we'll be glad to do it for you. Give us a sign."

"Hey, c'mon guys, it's almost finished and we'll have fun roughing it—-right?" said the accursed nephew. I rose slowly and faced him, my nose covered in mud and with blood in my eye. "Does your uncle know that most dwellings have more than one wall braced up with two-by-fours and a plywood floor?" I screamed.

"Well, it has a floor and a roof" he replied as he cautiously backed up. "What more do we need?"

"You call that assemblage of scrap lumber a roof? I've seen better roofs on burnt-out warehouses."

Faced with three armed and potentially dangerous foes, he managed to convince us that it would be better to spend the night rather than attempt to return to the car in the dark in such weather. Building a fire in a 55 gallon trash barrel full of Dixie cups, half-eaten fast food hamburgers and scraps of roofing shingles, we wrapped ourselves in the meager coverings we had brought and huddled around the smelly warmth like delinquent trolls at the county dump. By 2:00 a.m. we were seriously considering feeding the fire with sections of the floor and by 6:00 a.m. we had to fight down an insane urge to set the whole thing ablaze and get a little warmth before beginning the trek back.

At daybreak, it was agreed to do a little hunting, therefore salvaging a portion of the nightmare. Sitting on the edge of the floor, our feet hanging over the river bluff, we waited for anything to walk by that would be dumb enough to venture out on such a day. After an hour I struggled stiff legs under me and announced that even if a deer large enough to pull the Budweiser wagon walked by, I wouldn't think about harming a local resident that had the courage to live like that every night.

What species other than homo sapiens would attempt to survive on a bitter night wrapped in a cloud of smoke generated by smoldering Dixie cups, old peanut butter sandwiches and six-month old copies of The American Handyman for the sake of a few pounds of meat in the freezer? I finally realized that hunting for food is fine, but if you're not hungry, try the meat department at your local grocer, buy a rack from an antique dealer and use your bow for hanging wet socks to dry. You'll live longer.

A TREE CLIMBING KAYAK

(Hot air balloons and kayaks have a lot in common. If there's no return transportation waiting for you when you reach your destination, the only choice is to put a "for sale" sign on the thing and hitch-hike home.)

I've had a few encounters with various types of water craft, mostly as a passenger in someone else's boat. There have also been attempts, disastrous I might add, at a jet ski and wind surfing. As for the jet ski, it had a nasty habit of bolting off like a race horse out of a starting gate and leaving me behind, while the wind surfer was like standing on a two-by-four in a hurricane. Admittedly, a little bit of dexterity is required for either craft.

The jet ski was one of those early models that required kneeling in a rear compartment, then standing when it planed out. I wouldn't know about the standing part because I never got past the kneeling stage. The thing would skip out from under me, leaving me flapping along behind like a wet grass sack for about twenty yards before I'd part company with it.

After swimming back to shore for the 10th time I asked if anyone had a rifle, preferably one in .270 caliber or larger. Through narrowed eyes the owner asked, "Why?" I explained that I didn't think anything in a smaller caliber would be effective if the thing decided to turn back and attack me.

"On the other hand, let's put it out of its misery now," I said. He put me on the windsurfer.

A dozen dunkings later I stood on it, 100 yards offshore, with no chance of getting back by tacking into the wind, waiting to be towed in. "What fun," I grumbled. "I'm sticking to motorcycles. They're safer."

A year later I relented to the siren song of watery adventure and invested in an aquatic motivation device when I swapped a few pieces of electronic gear for a friend's two-man kayak. With only two moving parts (me and whoever was dumb enough to join me), the only requirements for going in the desired direction were six inches of water and a little coordination with the double bladed paddles. Dave (my friend and former owner of the sleek craft) took on the task of showing me how to avoid decapitating my shipmate with the sharp edged paddles while at the same time moving in some direction other than circles. He explained that circles were nice when needed, but straight lines were necessary when leaving a dock. I should have realized that my instructor was a man who, besides being a fine engineer, was also a motorcycle freak. As anyone knows, motorcyclists live in a fantasy world where nothing can go wrong and who also think Evil Knievel was a chicken for wearing a parachute while attempting to jump the Grand Canyon.

This was the same guy who, while kick-starting an old Harley, advanced the spark too far and was lofted over the handlebars onto his head when the thing kicked back. I was entrusting my life to a man with a flat head as we launched ourselves into the raging waters of the Whitewater River.

We worked with a finely honed precision for the first three feet of the trip, until I took my first stroke with the paddle – on the wrong side of the boat. Eskimos will tell you that paddle coordination is critical to moving in the direction you wish to go. Since neither Dave nor myself are Eskimos, he didn't inform me of that. As a result, our paddles tangled and he got a thorough soaking when I tried to correct and slapped a paddle into the water on the other side of the boat.

With the same patience as trying to teach a hog how to dance ballet, he carefully explained the proper procedures for kayak propulsion. He also emphasized how dangerous it would be for me if I were to get him wet again. We moved another twenty feet and crossed paddles again. I began to wonder how Eskimos managed to get close enough to seals and walruses to feed and clothe their families, what with all the cussing and yelling that goes on when two people try to make one of those skinny boats go in a straight line.

Grumbling under our breath, we moved off again while I vowed that if Dave yelled at me one more time I would blow a hole in his end of the boat and laugh hysterically as he sank. Eventually, we managed to go for minutes at a time without tangling paddles or drenching each other.

Finally enjoying the quiet solitude of the stream, I noticed disturbances in the water ahead that marked the presence of underwater pilings left over from an old railroad bridge while Dave explained the necessity of avoiding them. We didn't. Our captain told me to get on the paddle hard and I did, but again, on the wrong one. The boat was made from a tough, plastic coated canvas stretched over spars and ribs and when we slid up on a piling it was like being blind-sided in the bum by a fence post.

From the commotion that followed, you would have thought I had invited his mother-in-law to dinner without his permission.

"I told you to dig in hard," he yelled.

"I did," I replied.

"I meant on the other side," he snarled.

"Well, next time say THE OTHER SIDE."

We rocked ourselves off the piling and continued in stony silence. A short time later a deep, slow moving pool gave us the chance to discuss our strategy (agreeing not to kill each other until we were safely ashore) and to take a cooling dip in the frigid water. On our way once again, we approached a narrow chute only ten or twelve feet wide, through which the water was rushing, deep and fast. A large tree had washed into the chute and lodged with its branches laying downstream and the trunk about a third of the way into the chute.

Captain Dave called for a pause and instructed me on the proper method of getting around the tree by applying strong paddle force on the left side as we entered the chute. "Ar, Cap'n, Ar" I growled as we sped into the chute and fairly flew up the tree until three-fourths of the 17-foot long boat balanced precariously high and dry on the trunk.

Through clenched teeth and white lips Dave said don't move and why didn't I dig in like I was told. Also through clenched teeth and white lips I replied that I had dug in and that it was not my fault. Hissing through compressed lips he said he meant back-paddle, not a forward stroke. As my teeth crumbled from the pressure I said next time say back-paddle. We managed by some miracle to rock the thing off the tree and stay upright while losing nothing but our lunch sacks.

The rest of the trip was no more eventful than hunting grizzlies while buck naked and armed only with sharp sticks. Our friendship survived and we spent pleasant hours that summer, floating the river and acting like Laurel and Hardy. I did learn a valuable lesson. Always listen to someone who knows the score, especially if he's a motorcyclist and is armed with a kayak paddle.

PIERCED EARS AND FISHING WITH MA BELL

(Two significant events occurred in man's past history. First, he stood upright. Then he spread his hands apart to show the size of the big one that got away.)

The discovery that fish are edible was the turning point in our ability to distinguish between the truth and the need to stretch credibility with libelous accounts of huge aquatic creatures last seen on the end of a fishing line. We've all had to suffer through stories that should have seen the perpetrator being arrested for creating aggravated mental anguish in the listener.

Perhaps the day will come when psychologists will determine what primal urge causes the otherwise normal angler to describe a six-inch bluegill as a ten pound monster with the personality of a pit bull. Perhaps a few incidents not involving an innocent fish would be refreshing.

My father-in-law and I spent many hours fishing a lake located on a military installation, that due to access restrictions to civilian liars, normally produced plenty of action. Burl was a creature of habit who believed it was our responsibility to arrive at his favorite spots before any fish with an average IQ was awake. I felt otherwise.

Being awakened at 3:00 a.m. to drive thirty miles, hauling a hundred pounds of gear to catch ten pounds of fish, if we were lucky, while sitting in a boat half filled with cold water, sometimes in an equally cold rain, was about as much fun as being skinned alive. By sunrise however, my mood normally changed as I entered into the spirit of things and began enjoying the solitude and scenery of the surrounding territory.

One Saturday, by mid-morning, I grew bored with watching motionless bobbers and decided to exercise my fly rod, an otherwise useless tool on these waters. With no ambitions of snagging anything in the deep water we were anchored in, I began trying for a personal best in long distance casting. To the discomfort of Burl who was sitting behind me, I whipped the rod over our heads time and again until a huge loop of line had the little barbed missile whistling by us like a demented bee.

Burl was a quiet man, never one to voice his opinion, especially when in the presence of an idiot armed with a fly rod. Finally, a forward cast resulted in a sudden stoppage and the line fell into the water in a wad. Thinking the lure had tipped the water behind me I began whipping the rod in an attempt to roll cast it back into action. From behind me came a calm voice informing me that I might want to hold up for a while because the fly was attached to his ear. Turning, I saw the fly hanging from an ear lobe like a feather covered bauble on an older hippie.

After trying unsuccessfully to smooth over the situation by telling him he didn't put up much of a fight, I removed the hook and left him with a perfectly pierced ear lobe. For some reason he failed to see the humor in my offer to pierce the other one for half price.

River fishing has always been one of my least favorite angling endeavors due to the methods and equipment commonly used. Heavy, non-flexible rods with a line capable of holding a mule tied to a tree, complete with 20 pounds of lead sinkers to hold against the current, and hooks as big as shark gaffs made me wonder what was out there that required such formidable gear. I considered a ball bat as necessary to subdue whatever was hauled from the water before being loaded into the bed of a pick-up for a trip to the butcher shop.

The ritual was as follows: load as many night crawlers as the hook would hold, place your thumb on the spool to act as a drag, fling it over your shoulder and watch as your thumb caught fire from holding pressure on the spool and hope a crows nest wouldn't develop in the line. Should that happen, the sudden stop of all that mass would either snap the line or send the fisherman scrambling out of the way of the rapidly returning buzz saw of sinkers and worm filled hooks.

There followed hours of boredom while waiting for something to swim by and become entangled in the unappetizing mess. When nothing happened I would begin reeling in every five minutes to "check the bait". More often than not the line would snag the bottom irretrievably and require a new rig of hooks, worms, and lead be installed. I've often visualized the river bottom looking like a spider web of fishing line with at least 20 tons of accumulated lead sinkers poisoning the water downstream.

In spite of the sophistication of this method of fishing, I was to learn at an early age a more technologically advanced method of outsmarting the scaly set. My father and three other "sportsmen" took me along on a fishing trip that involved no rods, bait, or lead sinkers. Aboard two old wooden flat bottomed boats, the only fishing gear appeared to be an ancient electrical contraption enclosed in a wooden box with a crank handle protruding from one side.

I remembered seeing one of those things in a Laurel and Hardy movie and asked what they intended to do with an old crank telephone.

"The fish today will be supplied by Ma Bell," replied one of the felons.

I watched as two wires were lowered overboard and one of the sportsmen began cranking furiously on the handle. The others stood by with long handled landing nets.

I've never seen such frenzied activity in the so-called sport of fishing. Fish would break the surface and skitter around the boats as nets and elbows flailed the air trying to snare the prizes of modern fishing technology. With the boats rocking precariously, I hoped the fools swinging the nets would fall overboard first because I wasn't sure but that they would get the same treatment as the fish. I visualized them screeching and walking on water to escape the electrical shocks.

After numerous attempts at different spots, not a fish had answered the phone and joined us in the boats. Trying to net one of those high voltage goosed victims required a deft hand with the awkward nets. As for me, I was hoping I was too young to be held as an accomplice, especially after turning states witness and helping to convict these miscreants. It was explained to me that the whole thing had been in fun and wasn't meant to influence my future fishing methods.

It did. Any fool could see that it would be a whole lot simpler to cut sticks of dynamite in quarters, tape them to rocks and throw them from the bank. Although that method would be a little noisier, it would eliminate the danger of being electrocuted. Also, you're not polluting the river with lead sinkers.

FISHING FOR PREHISTORIC SPECIES DISGUSTUS

(In spite of popular opinions within certain circles, there are some things best left out of the frying pan, such as hog jewels and certain species of fish.)

Through the process of natural evolution most species on this planet have physically changed over the eons. But, in spite of Mother Nature's skill in working to keep her creatures up with the times, a few examples have remained essentially unchanged, having been given everything necessary for survival, right from the start. Many examples of this exist, primarily in the form of reptiles and certain types of fish. The shark for instance, has changed little over the ages, and according to the experts, opossums are a direct link to the Jurassic Age.

Knowing this I walked around a couple of local bodies of shallow water that are best known for their ability to raise Boone and Crocket trophy sized mosquitoes. I ambled down to the water and watched as carp the size of Volkswagens rooted around the bank like hogs at a feed trough. The sight of them brought back memories of past experiences with these hardy throwbacks to the ice ages. With tears in my eyes I recalled the moments of excitement as I fought one to the bank and marveled at the sleek lines and handsome features of the species Slimus Disgustus. What other fish could offer such sport for no more than the cost of a half-pound of dough balls?

Some time later, my introduction to trying to catch the things came when a friend asked if I would care to join him in a night of fishing for something I thought would be better taken with a 30-06 from 300 yards away. Actually, I had spent more than one day stalking them in a quarry hole armed with a bow to which was attached a reel and a huge fiberglass fishing arrow. I had decided that if I nailed one I would cut the line and leave the fish, arrow and all. Fishing arrows were expensive, but I had been told that retrieving one from a carp was the same as pulling it out of a 30-year-old outhouse. Fortunately for me and the carp, I couldn't hit a school bus from ten feet with the thing, so I was spared the need to make a choice.

In spite of my misgivings, and in spite of being shocked at discovering my buddy would stoop to such a lowly thing as fishing for carp, I accepted. When I asked him what he planned to do with them if we got unlucky and snagged a few, he replied, "We'll put them on a stick, roast them over a fire and eat them. I call that carpsicles."

He almost lost me there, but when he explained that a neighbor wanted a few for his pond I relaxed. To quell my fears of being exposed to real fishermen, he said we would fish at night at a secluded spot on a large reservoir in an area where the chances of meeting anyone were very remote.

As we drove to the lake I envisioned a photographer for one of those slander magazines jumping out of the weeds and taking a picture just as I hauled a fish out of the water. It would appear on the front page under a headline that read "Trout Nut Collars Carp. World Aghast As Sportsman Surrenders To Trash Fish Temptress".

By 9:00 p.m. we were sitting at his favorite spot listening to the sounds of a large body of water at night. Frogs croaked and an occasional splash signaled the demise of another insect to a finned predator. Earlier, Dave had reluctantly revealed the ingredients in his secret dough ball recipe. It sounded so good that I suggested we start a fire and bake a few biscuits. Why waste it on a fish that probably wouldn't appreciate his culinary abilities?

"Common dough balls will lose more fish than they catch," he explained.

When I asked why, he said, "because when the fish take it and it sticks to the roof of their mouth they spit it out. After all, did you eat any of your mother's biscuits when they had the consistency of wallpaper cleaner? A carp has a little bit of class, too." I should have known better than ask a question of someone who fishes for a critter that even a snake refuses to associate with.

Just when I thought we might get lucky and avoid catching one I felt a tug on my pole. Instinctively, and before I had a chance to think, I set the hook. Whoa! The thing had a lot of spirit. The rod bent and the struggle between man and prehistoric beast was on. I forgot about such terms as "bottom grubbing scum sucker" and trash fish as I skidded a three-pounder onto the grass. As it lay flopping and squirming, reality returned and I refused to touch it for fear of catching some incurable disease. Dave, apparently used to handling fish that looked like a downspout covered with small shingles, grumbled something about over-aged wimps, unhooked it and dropped it into a water filled bucket.

During the rest of the night we caught enough to satisfy his neighbor and convince me that even if the things had a bad reputation, just like a toothless old bear, they were a lot of fun to wrestle with. However, one question came to mind. How come I've never seen one mounted on a plaque and displayed in someone's trophy room? Could it be because they couldn't explain the bullet hole? The more I thought about it, the more compassionate I felt toward these outcasts of the water world. An ugly duckling by any vote, but just like Mortimer Snerd, they must serve a purpose in nature's grand scheme. Perhaps if we re-named them, they might find an acceptable place in fish society. After all, what bass or bluegill would want to associate with something called a "carp"? Just change places with the two middle letters of the name and you have a totally different meaning.

RUSH HOUR FISHING

(For most fishermen, one of the important things is finding a spot that's quiet, secluded, and free of competition. Then you have the people who stand on bridges and fish while speeding cars blow their shirttail up their back. I guess it all depends on whether you prefer to snag a tree or a Toyota with your back cast.)

Returning to North Carolina's Outer Banks after the last visit twenty years ago I'm disappointed, but not surprised. On the previous trip I was dismayed at seeing the dunes along the shores being swallowed up by developers in their rush to satisfy the demand for hotels and condominiums. At that time there were still a few places where one could catch a glimpse of the beaches between buildings and only one out of five seagulls were addicted to potato chips and pepperoni pizza. It was still possible, using a surf rod, to fling a mess of foul smelling shrimp bait and a huge triangular sinker into the water and enjoy the sight of crashing surf while waiting for something stupid to swim by and become entangled in your rig. Those days are gone.

Today, those few gaps on the dunes are closed and for miles the only sight is a wall of architecturally ugly, hurricane-proof wonders. The beaches are inhabited by hoards of sun worshippers and any finned resident has to dodge a deluge of surfers and swimmers. In spite of such handicaps, there are a few diehard fishermen who, daily, set up their rigs and attempt to snare a denizen of the deep.

As I sat on the deck of our condo overlooking this scene, by observation I learned some of the secrets of surf fishing in the most trying of conditions. There are sections of beaches on the southern parts of the peninsula that are less crowded, but it seems that once the local fishermen learn how to fish in the more popular tourist sections they are reluctant to drive those distances. Maybe it has something to do with the number of bikinis lying on the sand. And, maybe part of the fun is having people stop and ask, "you ketchin' anything?" Even though those of us from the Midwest who might surf fish once every twenty years aren't too interested in the sport, it doesn't hurt to have a little knowledge of the proper techniques if you plan to try it. Here's what I observed.

Equipment requirements are simple. A rod, twelve feet long and about the size and stiffness of a fence post at the butt with a gargantuan open bail spinning reel and a rod holder to jam into the sand to start. These items can either be purchased or rented at places such as Black Beards Bait And Tackle or Cap'n Harry's Surf Board And Tackle And Beach Umbrella Shop, who also rent bicycles to older people. Next, a rig consisting of two hooks and a monstrous sinker attached to a wire for the benefit of those sea critters with teeth. Bait can either be shrimp or squid, depending on which you prefer for supper if the fish aren't biting. Finally, the properly equipped surf fisher carries along a folding chair, an ample amount of sun blocker to smear on his or her nose and a dog, preferably something large like a yellow

Lab or any other short haired variety large enough to pull a pony cart.

I'm not sure why the dog has to be a big one, but since it seems to be the standard I'll accept it. Perhaps the dog has to be big enough to protect the fisherman from anything he pulls in that has teeth and a nasty disposition.

Fishing in a crowd, especially among people who wouldn't know a treble hook from a pipe wrench requires a certain degree of skill. Bystanders tend to watch you cast by standing directly behind you. Sometimes a surfer runs directly in front of the fisherman just as he prepares to launch the rig. Here is where quick reflexes come into play as the fisherman, unable to stop his swing, releases the line at the top of the arc, sending the rig shooting straight up. He is then required by the code of ethics to shout "INCOMING" loud enough to be heard by any gawker standing within range of the descending mess of hooks and sinker.

Another problem involves the line already in the water and a kid on a boogy board with a short attention span. Skimming on the sand at the edge of the surf, a sand boarder can catch the line just about neck level and garrote himself. Also, elderly beach walkers tend to walk with their heads down, looking for shells, and seldom notice any obstructions in their path. Should one of them become entangled in the line, the fisherman could be in for a lot of misery from a beating with a cane or sun umbrella.

To avoid that possibility, the fisherman should attach a large orange flag to the line. This method works well for the surfer but is somewhat ineffective for the elderly walker who seldom looks up. Here, the best choice for a dog is an Australian sheep dog, trained to herd at command. When an unobservant pedestrian is sighted, simply sic the dog on him and herd him around behind the rod and line.

Should the fisherman be unfortunate enough to actually hook a surfboard or swimming suit, don't set the hook (actually, it would be fun to jerk a surfboard from under its rider and yell "Get A Job" at the top of your lungs). Tell the swimmer not to fight and you'll reel him in carefully. If the hook should snag part of a two-piece swim suit on a young lady, cut the line, quickly grab up your gear, call the dog and run. No excuse will be good enough for the beach patrol guys.

Surf fishing can be a rewarding and exciting sport if done properly. You probably won't catch anything, but the enjoyment of swapping lies with other fishermen and being with your dog will be a day well spent.

One other factor to keep in mind. If you should catch something, the sight of your dog attacking a critter you've drug from the surf might incite angry reactions from the sun bathers. If that possibility exists, take along your short-haired pointer and teach him to point anything over twelve inches long. Then tell the bathers that you are from the Midwest. It works every time.

A FROG BY ANY OTHER NAME

(Bear huntin' with wet powder is like invitin' your mother-in law over for a weekend. Either way, you know you're gonna end up bein' chewed on.)

The real outdoorsman is one who truly appreciates nature and spends as much time as possible enjoying it. Sitting in quiet solitude on the edge of a farm pond with a ten dollar fishing pole in your hand and a two dollar dog at your side is indeed quality time. The sight of a good pointer or setter on hard point and the anticipation of trying to explain the reason for missing another clear shot to your hunting partner is sheer pleasure. There are some outdoor activities that rank above all others for blood pounding excitement and kicks and giggles, while others seem like quilting bees. I got involved in one that I thought would be comparable to a snoring contest and found out that you can't judge a rattlesnake by the smile on its face.

A friend of mine asked if I would like to accompany him on a nighttime frog hunt on one of the local creeks. Now, my idea of fun doesn't include wading around in a shallow mud-bottom creek at midnight carrying a miniature pitch fork and trying to stick it into a green, slime covered, bug-eyed critter that spends its time sitting in cold water sounding like a kid with the croup. Frog legs are a delicacy, but if I have to collect the food, and there's a choice between frog and chicken legs, I'll take a shotgun into the chicken coop every time. It's easier.

The only excuse I could think up quickly was that my gall bladder had been acting up lately and I was planning to make an appointment to have it removed that afternoon.

"No problem," he said. "Forget the appointment and we'll kill two birds with one stone (poor choice of words). We'll go frogging tonight, and tomorrow you show me where it is and I'll remove the thing." Since he apparently wasn't going to take no for an answer, I bought a gig, cut the handle off a broom and attached the gig to the end of it. Armed to the teeth and prepared to do battle with the wily bull frog, I stood in front of a mirror and surveyed the sight of the average frogger.

Ratty old sneakers, no socks, battered blue jeans, a T-shirt I had planned to use as a car polishing rag, and a multi-pronged spear gave me the appearance of Lucifer after a bad Saturday night on the town.

"You'd better put on socks," said my buddy.

"Why?" I asked. "The water should be pretty warm this time of year."

"Leaches," he answered. "The socks might help keep them off, at least for a while."

"Whoa, whoa, Kemosabe," I snarled. "What's this with leaches? I'd rather pull a good-sized water moccasin off my bum than a leach off my leg. A frog big enough to pull a hay wagon isn't worth a leach on the leg. Besides, I don't donate blood to the Red Cross, much less to a bunch of mindless vampires."

"Calm down," he said. Pulling out a big, black cigar he explained how he would use it to remove any that I picked up.

"Just great," I whined. "Not only will I have sucker marks all over me, you're going to add a few cigar burns to them." If I had been a runner I would have worn my heel to neck Spandex tights as protection.

Standing on the creek bank I shined my light into the dark, sluggish water, looking for what I knew was a two-foot long leach just waiting for me. As I slid in I began whapping the surface with the gig and shouting, "Hyaa——Hyaa." My partner (he stopped being a friend an hour before) shouted, "Whaddya doing?"

"Clearing a path through this leach farm," I replied. After he explained the effect such action had on frogs I resigned myself to my fate and we started wading upstream, shining our lights on the bank and listening for the melodious call of the amorous, web-footed amphibians. As we crept slowly along I remembered years before when I had participated in a hunt where one man scanned the bank of a pond with a flashlight, while another served as the hit man, armed with a .32 caliber revolver. I was the bag man, responsible for retrieving the deceased in case the gunman got lucky and hit one. Surprisingly enough, we dined on a nice mess of legs that evening in camp, but I had a difficult time digesting a meal that kept trying to climb out of the skillet. It's true that frog legs will move around for some time after being separated from the rest of the carcass. I'm not used to eating game that has to be chased around the plate.

By now up to our waist in the water and finally getting into the spirit of the hunt, I began looking in earnest for victims. Then, a question came to mind. Does the hunter try to get close enough to stick a frog or does he throw the thing at it?

"Sneak in as close as you can and jab him," the frog man answered.

Now enlightened on the proper procedure we continued, our flashlight beams revealing nothing on the bank. Suddenly, a pair of sparkling eyes began moving toward us across the surface and was soon joined by two or three other pairs. Frogs?

"Naw, just snakes," said frog man casually.

Two things happened simultaneously. I forgot all about leaches and then proceeded to break all standing records held by only one other in walking on water. Standing on the bank I explained to frog man that he was now on his own and that if I had any leaches on me, we would both be going to the hospital. Me to get my gall bladder removed and him to have a three-pronged spear jerked out of his posterior.

Since that night I've enjoyed frog legs, but they've been served to me by someone named Pierre in a four star restaurant. Expensive, but served without leaches and snakes.

A LATE NIGHT RODENT AND JOCKEY SHORTS

(Sometimes you wonder where rodents fit into Mother Nature's grand plan. Maybe they're meant to keep owls and hawks fat and happy. Then, maybe they're good for nothing but making heroes out of men while the ladies stand on chairs, screaming.)

I've often wondered what's so special about small, four-legged fuzzy critters that causes women to go into hysterics and allow pest exterminators to drive Cadillacs. I've never seen a rodent that was big enough to drag a person into its den and eat him, but I've witnessed the result of, say a mouse, running across the floor of the Second United Baptist Church ladies club meeting. You could turn an alligator loose in Bubba's Bar and Grill and not empty a room faster.

I've had my share of run-ins with the little terrorists, and more times than not, I've been the first critter caught when the mouse trap mis-fires prematurely. Nothing starts the day like finding a hole in the side of the cereal box and knowing that mice are not too particular about where they go potty. Normally, I live by the motto, "live and let live", but when any species of the family genus *Rodentia* starts messing around with my personal property, it's all-out war.

After spending almost three years of hard manual labor constructing a log cabin deep in the woods, I get a little touchy even when the wind blows and I watch over it like a grizzly tending her cubs. Even though it's located fourteen miles from what we call home, I can hear moles burrowing around it and by sniffing the air I can determine if the outhouse is over-percolating.

One fall afternoon as I sat at a picnic table at the cabin admiring the changing colors of the surrounding trees, the ground in front of me began heaving up and down. There is no yard to speak of, but the moles had the place looking like it had been strip mined by a bunch of midget coal miners.

Slowly, I drew my trusty shootin' arn and hissed, "Okay you little subterranean, grub eating devil. Ah'm a'gonna part your hair." Nine rapid shots later, all I had to show for it was a small patch of chewed-up real estate followed by a temper tantrum. Those things can disappear faster than money on the stock market. And, they do it in the dirt. I finally decided that as long as it wasn't undermining the foundation of the cabin and was able to dodge nine rounds from "old sure shot", I'd leave it alone. However, I figured to get real mean when another variety rubbed my fur the wrong way.

On certain occasions I had awakened in the wee hours to hear little yellow teeth gnawing on woodwork, somewhere around the eves of the cabin. Stumbling from bed in the sleeping loft I would pound on the ceiling and the chewing would stop. The next morning an outside inspection revealed areas of tooth marks on the siding at the peak of the roof. I figured it was a chipmunk, but how did the little devil manage to climb a vertical surface and hang onto it while chewing. Besides, what was there about grooved barn siding, especially the chemically treated kind that appealed to a rodent?

A week went by, and again late at night, I awoke to the sounds of little incisors attempting to reduce the place to sawdust. Repeated poundings on the ceiling failed to stop it.

My wife, awakened to the noise, asked whether I was trying to stop the chewing or tear the place down with my bare hands. I grabbed a flashlight, and wearing only my BVD's and a pair of unlaced tennis shoes, sneaked out the back door. We had been feeding a friendly raccoon and a handful of dog biscuits, the size for dogs of fifty to seventy pounds, were still lying on the patio deck. I picked them up to throw, just in case I got a shot at the four-legged chain saw. I figured they would be better than blowing holes in the roof overhang, especially after the mole incident.

Slowly and quietly I sneaked around the corner of the cabin and flashed the light toward the eves. There, clinging to the siding was a flying squirrel, looking like a miniature cat burglar, its eyes glowing red in the beam and obviously now blinded and confused. I threw a dog biscuit at it and shouted, "Gidd-ouda-here you little tree climbing rat." I'm no better with dog biscuits than I am with a handgun, so I chucked another one. That Pet Smart bullet almost connected and the little assassin scampered across the overhang and onto the roof where it sat peeking over at me.

"Go ahead, make my day," I snarled. It began running up and down the roof, occasionally peeking over to see if its assailant was still interested in raising knots on its head. Obviously terrified, it launched itself off the roof and sailed over my head as I tried to follow it with the light. It hit the ground and scampered into the woods with me on its heels, flinging dog biscuits and screaming profanities as I crashed through a stand of small maple trees. I quickly discovered that when it comes to speed, flying squirrels make moles look like 90 year-old stock car drivers.

As it disappeared, I stopped, panting and covered with scratches from small limbs and briars. Suddenly, it dawned on me that I was standing in the woods at 2:00 a.m. wearing nothing but my Fruit Of The Looms and unlaced tennis shoes, armed with a single round of heavy caliber dog biscuit and probably about to step on the tail of a Bengal tiger. Two seconds later and back inside, my wife asked anxiously, "What was it, dear?" I sniffed, pushed out my chest and said, "a badger, and a big one. But, don't worry. I took care of it." I laid the single remaining round on the night stand for protection against any further incidents and slept soundly, knowing we were now well protected by a 30-06 dog biscuit and a naked nut.

WHAT GOES AROUND, COMES AROUND

(It gets real depressing when, if you can't even turn the darn thing on, you have to ask a six year old where the switch is.)

In the final stages of assembly, it bore a faint resemblance to a dismembered swamp creature equipped with a gaping mouth lined with red plastic and bulbous evil eyes. The only semblance of a body ended behind the head where a plastic frame surrounded what looked like the trigger on a bear trap. Next out of the box came a plastic golf club and two balls. The final step was to install the usual batteries and Gator Golf was ready for action.

The four year old carefully aligned his shot and after a dozen tries finally managed to whack the ball into the gator's mouth. The ball passed through the head and fell into the bear trap, which promptly flipped it over its head and back to the putter. Then, the head began spinning and came to a stop facing away from the player.

"That looks real exciting, David," I said to my grandson, "but what else does it do?"

"Nothing Papaw, it just poops the ball back to you."

"That's interesting," I said. "Do you get a kick out of swinging a golf club at alligator poop?"

This small attempt at humor produced nothing more than a momentary blank stare and then a return to swatting the ball and retrieving it when it missed. Shortly afterwards, the two year old stepped on it and rendered it poopless.

After a half-hour of watching various items being cleaned off the coffee table and shins being whacked by the swinging golf club, I idly picked up another electronic device that belonged to the twelve year old. Called a Game Boy, it consisted of a plastic case containing a maze of miniature circuits and a small liquid crystal video screen. A trap door on one side allowed a small cassette to be inserted, apparently allowing a player to participate in some kind of game.

I wouldn't know about that. Five minutes of pushing buttons and uttering words that would have started a bulldozer produced nothing as the thing lay there like a cancelled postage stamp. "I'm a grown man," I muttered, "and if I have to sit here until midnight I will not ask Matt how to turn it on."

I had to. It resisted every effort to bring it to life until I finally screamed, "Matt, this @^$%#& thing was made by a company called DIABOLICAL MANUFACTURING UNLIMITED and it won't turn on." He sighed, made a mystical movement over it with his hand and the screen came to life. For the next ten minutes I watched as the accursed thing played all by itself because I couldn't get it to respond to anything I pushed, pulled, or tugged.

"MAAAATT, HOW DO YOU GET THIS THING TO INCLUDE ME IN THE GAME?" Once again, he manipulated the controls while it made little squeaks and bloops and finally introduced me to the rules to follow. Wiping away tears, I held it close to my mouth and hissed, "Look, you little offspring of a demented ivory tower egghead, I'm giving you five seconds to tell me what to do next or you'll end up in the microwave with the timer set on meatball casserole."

It shut itself off. While I lay on the floor sobbing, Matt brought me a Nerf ball and bat, told me to be careful with it and not hurt myself, and took the demon possessed little electronic monster out of my limp hand. I hate toy companies.

Back home that evening, technologically exhausted, I couldn't wait to install a laser sight I had received as a gift from my wife, on my favorite hand gun. No doubt, here was something I could handle. After all, aren't target shooters supposed to be adept and skilled at handling their equipment?

Unpacking the thing I sorted through a small pile of little pieces that would allow it to be mounted on a variety of firearms, picked out those for my model and set to work. An hour later as I lay face down on the floor, my chest heaving in racking sobs, I cried, "It won't fit. Call Matt and see how fast he can get here." Consoled and patted on the head, I was encouraged to try again by Judy. Finally, I had the little demon mounted. Now, all that remained was to install the batteries and get it adjusted so that the bullet would strike somewhere in front of me when fired.

At this point I should have remembered an old saying about giving an uneducated person an educated task. This little generator of a narrow beam of coherent light had warnings all over it to avoid directing the beam into an eye. Fiddling with the adjustments I accidentally turned it on and a brilliant red beam entered my left cornea, traveled up the optic nerve, short-circuited the common sense module in my brain, and set the hair on the back of my head on fire. Now with a bright red spot permanently in my vision, I figured, what the heck. I don't use that eye for shooting, and I might look pretty dashing wearing a pirate's eye patch.

By this time the average person would have sworn off anything more complex than a zipper, but I didn't know when to quit. Further complications developed when I decided to replace an old computer in my office, which incidentally could be out-smarted by a chimpanzee, with a more modern, updated version.

Maybe I couldn't handle a Game Boy, but computers were my slaves. As I stood in the electronics department of a large retail chain store, gazing at the bewildering array of processors and monitors, a salesperson asked if he could be of assistance. "Lemme look around and I'll call you if I need help," I answered. One CPU (computer processing unit) caught my eye with its racy lines and flashy color (black). Squaring my shoulders for effect, I began reading the specifications for the thing. My confidence began crumbling like the foundation under an old building. My lip began to quiver as I read:

200 MHz processor with MMX technology

128 MB SyncDRAM

40.0 GB Hard Drive

16X Max CD-ROM Drive and 256 KB L2 Pipeline Burst Cache

In smaller print was, "The K56flex protocol is designed only to allow faster downloads from K56flex compliant digital sources. SyncDRAM compared to EDO using Winstone 32 benchmark. 16x Max CD-ROM drive data transfer rates may vary from 1200 to 2400 Kbps.

Whaddit say? I sensed the "you're standing under a falling piano" module in my brain beginning to overheat. Just as I finished reading something about "maximum resolution", my mind snapped and the salesman touched me on the shoulder. "Would you like some help now?"

"Don't touch me, get away from me, you – you microchip brained android," I screamed as I began backing toward the door. Outside, I leaned against a wall and began gulping in big swallows of air while wondering what happened to simpler times. Glancing down I noticed the stub of a half-smoked cigar lying beside the curb. With lifted spirits I retrieved it, lit up and walked toward the car. Maybe there is still room in the world of technology for a good nickel cigar I thought, even though it was a little soggy and hard to light. After all, what goes around, comes around, and life is still good.

Dan Graves

OF SUMMER DAYS AND BUTTERFLIES

In a time of quiet reflection on a sultry summer night
In the gentle breeze and flickering
Of the fireflies soothing light

I felt the brush of gossamer wings – a ghost of yesterday
And heard once more the tiny voice
"Can he come out and play?"

Like a rainbow colored butterfly, it danced before my eye
To the sound of gay young laughter
'Neath a cloudless summer sky

Just beyond my reach it flew
Through the gardens in my mind
And left me running after what I knew I could not find

The boundless joys of childhood, like a rose at summer's end
Will remain forever out of reach
Like a distant, cherished friend

*The tarnished dreams of endless life and forever summer
days
Too soon will fade into the dusk
Of autumns twilight haze*

*Like dreams and fears and hopes and tears
And hurts your mother kissed
The butterfly begins to dim like dreamy summer mist*

*A final twinkling laughter echoes through the veils of time
Taunting like the beckon
Of a dancing, prancing mime*

*I turn to leave and glancing back
I listen for a sound
Oh Lord, Oh Lord, please tell me where I'm bound*

Dan Graves

PECKING ORDERS AREN'T JUST FOR CHICKENS

Most of us recall our youth with mixed emotions, ranging from a warm, glowing feeling of better days, to amazement that we survived to remember those warm, glowing feelings. One thing that did more than any other to assure survival was the necessity of knowing your place in the family hierarchy and taking pains to stay there. Most families were (and still are) much like a pack of wolves.

The father is the alpha male, the so-called lord over his domain, while the mother is the one with the real power, the disciplinarian who would drop-kick you into the next county if you got out of line. At the bottom of the heap were the children, who according to their age, maintained their own pecking order when the big ones weren't around.

The establishment of the corporate structure in our group was simple. My brother, by virtue of being the oldest, was the chief executive officer. I was his defiant subordinate, while our sister as the youngest proved to both of us that all that was needed to assume control of any situation was to run screaming to one of the big ones and point back at us while sobbing out something that sounded like, "He hit me with a two-by-four."

The normal reaction was for the CEO and I to stand shaking our heads and pointing at the other while the big one advanced on us like a steam roller preparing to crush a pair of tumblebugs. Afterwards, the two of us would discuss corporate policies, such as presenting our sister with a snake for her birthday, or perhaps refraining from beaning each other for trying to place the blame on the other.

We, the CEO and I, soon learned that if you were a delicate little girl, you held the majority of the stock in our corporation and maintained control of life or death over the other members of the board of directors. Normally, she didn't exercise her power to the fullest, but whenever she started to pucker her lips or whimper, we knew it was time for us to either pull her on the sled for a little while or resign ourselves to plucking chickens for a living.

The big ones assigned chores according to the physical requirements of the job. However, if the pigs had to be put back into the barn, I normally ended up facing the old sow like Arnold Stang staring down a bear while the CEO rounded up the piglets. He would explain to me that someone had to divert the attention of the old gal and that I was much quicker on my feet than he was, and that I should yell if she managed to get around me and go for him. That proved to be no problem. I would wait until the piglets were squealing adequately, give the old sow the raspberries and then head for the fence while yelling at the CEO that it looked like she was going to get around me.

She would home in on my brother like a fat, muddy tank on rusty treads, squealing and snorting while he joined me on the other side of the fence. There, we would stand with our hearts thumping and discuss our next move. I seldom voted in favor of these plans because they always involved my getting the old girl's attention, and while trying to stay ahead of her, leading her across the lot while the CEO herded the little ones into the barn.

These planning sessions always ended in heated arguments as to who was responsible for what, while the pigs continued to roam around the lot. There was no doubt as to who was the chairman of the board. It was the old sow.

Finally, the issue would be settled by the arrival of Mom (one of the big ones) who would bring a bucket of slop, thus getting the attention of the sow, who at this time could care less about her brood. As the hog dug into this delightful repast, Mom would calmly herd the piglets into the barn.

After informing us that it was a good thing the pork market didn't depend on us to bring in the product, she would again emphasize the need to distract the sow with food before trying to herd the litter. We would promise to do so the next time while knowing we wouldn't, because it was too much fun doing it our way.

The pecking order manifested itself in other ways, seemingly with those of us on the bottom of the corporate ladder always furnishing entertainment for those at the top. For instance, when it was time to throw clods at the beehives, the peons were elected as pitchers for the reason that we could run faster if need be. Logically, a race horse can't outrun a honked-off bee, but we weren't blessed with great amounts of logic.

The normal procedure was to sneak to the corner of the barn and peer around at the hives while the executives whispered encouragement to us from a safe distance. At the right moment, hoping to impress our superiors and maybe earn a promotion, we would wildly throw our missiles, turn and run back to the barnyard gate and wait to see if the attack produced results. If none of our victims showed up for revenge, we were encouraged to launch a second attack. If successful, we would all make a beeline (pun intended) for the house where one of the big ones would be waiting to convince us of the error of our ways. It was like taking refuge from a pack of wolves by hiding in a bear's den.

After being convinced that another such incident would result in the termination of all those involved, we would try to find something to take our mind's off the possibility that we were within a hair's breadth of having our little corporation falling victim to a hostile takeover.

Such plans normally ended with the CEO being placed in labor prison for life due to his lack of responsibility for his underlings, and I as his right hand man suffering the same fate if our little sister was involved in any way. How were we to know that smoking horse weed would make her sick, or that she would fall off a hay wagon so easily?

Ours was not the only such structured group in the neighborhood. There were a number of families who's CEO's occasionally joined forces with others to make life as miserable as possible for their underlings. Herded together, we were used as shark bait when swimming in the local quarry holes and as targets for dried meadow muffins in cow pie fights. Being outclassed and out-sized, we seldom fought back, but if outsiders picked on us, the chief's were quick to defend their Indians.

We endured it all though, hoping that some day we would have the nerve to splatter our CEO with a pail of fresh bovine excrement and live to tell the tale. Funny how, after a few years passed, I found out that the other members of our little corporation had turned out to be pretty nice people. But, it was only after we stopped flinging rotten eggs and cow dump at each other and switched to more adult types of fun. I got great pleasure from answering the phone when a boyfriend or girlfriend called and saying something like, "I'm sorry, but he (or she) is sitting in the outhouse reading the Sears and Roebuck catalog. May I take a message?"

AN AVERAGE DAY FOR THE TECHNONERD

In this day and age, I guess the best description for our humdrum lives is that we are technologically enhanced. What other words would describe the fact that practically everything we do involves a gadget (according to the sales pitch for that nifty little micro-processor controlled, maxi-digital display, super hetrodyne, phase adjusted, electronic spear sharpener) that will make our lives easier and simpler so that we will have time to enjoy the finer things of life.

Oh, yeah? I hate to be a spoilsport, but our in-house inventory of batteries of every size and description would power an aircraft carrier for six months of sea duty. Meanwhile, a number of ingenious devices are sitting on a closet shelf with their little micro-processors fried into oblivion. To test my dependence on electronic devices, I've even gone so far as attempting to add up a column of figures manually, using a pad of paper and a pencil without the aid of Texas Instrument. It isn't easy, especially since we no longer have a sixth-grader around to check the results.

We've also been brainwashed into believing that no efficient household is complete without a personal computer to handle our everyday affairs. Ours insists on doing things its way in spite of efforts to convince it that the bank balance doesn't belong in the column on the spreadsheet that says, "Things To Delete."

I enter "Save."

It asks, "Are You Sure?"

I reply, "Yep."

It replies, "Unknown Command. I/O Error. Deleting All Entries."

I enter, "Why, you no-good for nothing @#%&*."

It replies, "Unknown expletives. I/O Error. Deleting entire database."

I grab my Louisville Slugger baseball bat and attempt to end this miserable electronic life while my wife struggles to prevent me from destroying something on which we still owe twelve monthly payments.

Another technological wonder is the automobile that won't start because the mass fuel-air accelerometer data sensor is lying on its back with its little diodes sticking straight in the air. It takes a degree in advanced micro-nuclear physics just to find out where it's located and you're ten miles out in the middle of nowhere at midnight in a blinding blizzard.

AAARRRGH!

Considering our love of gadgetry (and the need to keep up with the Jones'), a normal day for the average citizen in our high tech society would probably go something like this.

Awakened by an alarm radio playing the latest release from "There's a Fly In Your Soup" by "Slimy Sid and The Scroungy Six,"the victim stumbles from bed and prepares to face a shower. Much to his or her dismay, the automatic temperature control adjustable flow rate inertial massage valve on the shower has been reset by one of the kids to the "red hot peel the skin off your back supersonic jet stream" setting.

With screams drowning out Slimy Sid, a day's accumulation of top soil and a layer of hide is flushed down the drain. Looking like something just taken from a lobster net in the North Sea, the victim plugs in the Acme four-axis reciprocating electronic tooth brush that is recommended by four out of five dentists (I wonder what the fifth one has to say about it) and proceeds to grind enamel and taste buds away in a bubbling foam of abrasive fluoride.

Next comes breakfast, prepared in a kitchen bristling with the latest in electronic marvels. Preparing oatmeal in the microwave oven produces a concoction that can be sliced with a knife and eaten with a fork. The toaster sets off the automatic smoke detector with flaming bread while the coffee maker spews out something that resembles roofing tar.

Properly nourished and ready to face the day, its off to the garage where the new Fireball ZXL990RS coupe with every option known to mankind awaits. The automatic garage door opener sends out its signal, shutting off the next door neighbors pacemaker and activating the no-jam screw drive door opener which promptly jams. The problem is quickly resolved by propping it open with the emergency linear cellulose non-adjustable door prop (two-by-four) and closed by a quick kick to same.

On the road, our hero turns on the super hetrodyne X, Y, and Z band radar detector that is so sensitive it can receive signals from another planet and heads for the interstate highway, confident in the fact that he can now safely travel forty miles an hour over the speed limit, thus avoiding being trampled in the stampede.

Buzzing along at speeds that would have won the Indy 500 in 1955 he remembers the phone call he promised to make yesterday. No problem. Using one hand to steer and one eye to watch the road, he uses the other pair to dial the multi-function 400 channel inductive amplified cellular phone.

Now listening to Mom explain the similarity of trying to drive a car and talk on the phone to walking and chewing gum at the same time, he misses his exit and drives five miles back to the office where he faces the epitome of modern technology, his lap top computer.

Considered as the most advanced on the market when purchased, it was obsolete when he walked out of the store. With 80 gigabytes of memory and loaded with every accessory program but one, he has discovered that without the latest download on ancient Egyptian history, he will not be competitive in today's market.

Placing a call to the Ancient Egyptian Software Co. he hears, "If you wish to speak to the Sphynx Department, press 1: If you wish to speak with Pyramids, press 2: "If you wish to speak to –," and so on for ten minutes. After placing the order he rests easy in the knowledge that he is now abreast of his competitors, that is after he orders the newest 120 gigabyte computer, complete with built-in stereophonic sound system and mega-mouse.

Back home, the evening meal is slid from its box and charred in the microwave as the family prepares to watch another two hours of sitcoms and three hours of commercials on t.v.

In bed, the average citizen can look back on another day of technological enhancement with a sense of satisfaction. He didn't get electrocuted, arrested for speeding, or scolded for forgetting to put the cat out before leaving for work. The timer controlled opener for the pet door worked perfectly. It just doesn't get any better than this.

Dan Graves

DANCING – FROM CAVEMAN TO COOLMAN

Fred Astaire, Gene Kelley, Mitzy Gaynor, Alfonso "Lumpy" Grundwich. These are just a few of the names known to all as people who danced their way to fame and fortune (in Lumpy's case the word is misfortune. He is well known as the first recorded person to dance to the old tune of "The .44 Caliber Blues" in front of the Grizzly Gulch saloon on the night of July 14, 1867 in Rumblegut, Texas after a dispute over the ownership of a mule. The orchestra conductor was Hezekiah Johnson, the mules other owner). For centuries, dancing has been a symbolic and ritualistic expression of love, war, and mankind's inability to sit still for more than ten minutes.

We dance at weddings, sometimes at funerals, and nowadays for no special reason other than to have fun, exercise our primordial need to express ourselves, or collect quarters in a hat on a street corner.

Dancing probably originated with cavemen who, lacking shoes, found that walking on hot rocks and through briar patches was a good reason to trip the light fantastic. Yelling "Ouch, Ooch, Yeeow" no doubt developed into a

208

beat that they related to the hopping motion, and a type of dancing was born that is still popular today.

During my impressionable years, I thought of dancing as something to avoid like the plague; a ritual that only creampuffs indulged in. However, Mom had other ideas and attempted to teach me ballroom dancing. Imagine trying to teach a chicken to balance a broom handle on its beak while walking a tight rope and juggling six eggs at the same time and you have an idea of her chances of success.

To this day the sound of a mambo, samba or waltz sends shivers down my spine and anchors my feet to the floor like magnets on a refrigerator door. If any of my buddies had shown up during one of our lessons I could have worn ballet slippers and a tutu to school and fared better than having been seen dancing with my Mom to The Blue Danube waltz. Mom also learned the difficulty of dancing with a partner who not only wouldn't lead, but had to be drug through all the motions with his toes scraping the floor.

My refusal to learn even the simplest of steps led to complications when I asked a girl to my first high school prom. Proms were no doubt dreamed up by a sadist who knew that the majority of teenage boys couldn't dance their way out of a sack full of bees, but who also couldn't resist the temptation of proving that fact to everyone in school, especially the poor girls who had to endure the brunt of such assaults.

The fateful night came and I stood at her door, corsage in hand and praying that the band would all be diagnosed at the last minute as carriers of leprosy or caught red-handed robbing a bank. Numerous excuses such as religious beliefs, an old war injury, or a complete disdain for such pagan ritualism crossed my mind, but I knew that my prowess with women would depend on other measures after tonight. Dancing wasn't going to win me any favors.

The band showed up (curse them) and I spent the first hour trying to drown my date with punch, hoping she would forget about dancing while spending the evening in the restroom. Finally, I had to submit to the inevitable. When she returned from the fourteenth trip to the bathroom, I asked if she would like to struggle. Her face lit up with shock and surprise and I led her onto the floor on feet that felt like trash can lids, muttering "One, two, three, step – One, two, three – ." After a few moments of awkwardness, I fell into the rhythm, recalling the steps to the Blue Danube that Mom had struggled to drill into me. My movements became fluid and graceful as we swept around the floor in a study of poetry in motion.

Okay, so the band was playing Elvis Presley's "Blue Suede Shoes", but I believe in the old saying of, Ya uses what ya got, not what ya oughta." As the last strains of the music ended and we glided to a stop, I noticed that we had a large portion of the floor to ourselves. Other dancers had stopped to watch our performance, no doubt envying my abilities and perhaps harboring just a little jealousy at being upstaged.

I must have impressed my date, because when I asked her out the following week, she politely declined and said that she didn't feel she was capable of learning how to dance the Mamba to "Peggy Sue". Some of us have it and some don't.

Some time later when the "twist" became popular and I found that gyrating hips were easier to coordinate than feet, I forgot about ballroom and and launched into wildly swinging elbows and "onfanosanatum" (Mom's favorite word for butt). A friend, observing a rather portly dancer do the twist, summed it up appropriately. "Kinda looks like two bears fightin' in a sack."

Most new dances last only months before being replaced by the latest fad, but Judy and I got in our licks before the twist faded. A resort hotel in the southern part of the state held Saturday night dances, complete with big bands playing the more popular music from the forties. We arrived that evening to find ourselves among a convention of what appeared to be The Royal Order Of Ancient Mariners, most of whom were at least three times our age. After an hour of sitting on the sidelines and watching the other couples sway to the strains of Jimmy Dorsey, I finally asked the band leader if he knew a twist tune. You bet, he answered and the group launched into Chubby Checker's "Let's Do The Twist."

No one moved. We finally decided to throw caution to the wind and go it alone. The ice was broken and within minutes the floor was a mass of shaking, rolling, bumping evening wear clad senior citizens doing their best to copy our movements with at least a semblance of class without throwing something out of joint. Seeing that the situation was getting out of hand, we stepped off the floor and watched as the generation gap disappeared in a crowd of grandparents swinging their hips and laughing at their so-called dignity.

Fascinated, we walked away muttering, "Man, that is outasight. Can you dig that scene? Those cats have got more steam than us. However, you won't catch me doin' the Charleston."

ABOUT THE AUTHOR

From Ninja chickens to not so slick moves at the drive-in theatre, the author shows that if you aren't having fun with life, you're probably dead. His philosophy is, "Even though I had nothing to say about the decision to bring me into this world, I'm going to take advantage of the opportunity. I'm also going to hunt down the guy who smacked me in the delivery room."

A freelance writer of a weekly newspaper column for ten years, six years as a columnist for a monthly outdoor publication, and a member of Hoosier Outdoor Writers, he attempts to describe the humorous side of everyday situations faced by the average Joe and Joan. A laugh at life.

Printed in the United States
25198LVS00002B/67-204